5 95
1

Ionic
Aliphatic
Reactions

Prentice-Hall Foundations of Modern Organic Chemistry Series

KENNETH L. RINEHART, JR., Editor

Volumes published or in preparation

N. L. ALLINGER and J. ALLINGER	**STRUCTURES OF ORGANIC MOLECULES** (1965)
CHAPMAN	**FUNCTIONAL GROUPS IN ORGANIC COMPOUNDS** (1966)
STEWART	**INVESTIGATION OF ORGANIC REACTIONS** (1965)
SAUNDERS	**IONIC ALIPHATIC REACTIONS** (1965)
GUTSCHE	**CHEMISTRY OF CARBONYL COMPOUNDS** (1965)
PRYOR	**INTRODUCTION TO FREE RADICAL CHEMISTRY** (1965)
STOCK	**AROMATIC SUBSTITUTION REACTIONS** (1965)
RINEHART	**OXIDATION AND REDUCTION OF ORGANIC COMPOUNDS** (1966)
DePUY	**MOLECULAR REACTIONS AND PHOTOCHEMISTRY** (1966)
IRELAND	**ORGANIC SYNTHESIS** (1965)
DYER	**APPLICATIONS OF ABSORPTION SPECTROSCOPY OF ORGANIC COMPOUNDS** (1965)
BATES and SCHAEFER	**RESEARCH TECHNIQUES IN ORGANIC CHEMISTRY** (1965)
TAYLOR	**HETEROCYCLIC COMPOUNDS** (1967)
HILL	**COMPOUNDS OF NATURE** (1965)
BARKER	**ORGANIC CHEMISTRY OF BIOLOGICAL COMPOUNDS** (1965)
STILLE	**INDUSTRIAL ORGANIC CHEMISTRY** (1966)
RINEHART and SIM	**X-RAY CRYSTALLOGRAPHY AND MASS SPECTROMETRY OF ORGANIC COMPOUNDS** (1966)

IONIC ALIPHATIC REACTIONS

William H. Saunders, Jr.

Professor of Chemistry
University of Rochester

PRENTICE-HALL, INC., ENGLEWOOD CLIFFS, N.J.

© 1965 by Prentice-Hall, Inc.

Library of Congress Catalog Card Number 65-11672
Printed in the United States of America
C-50605(p)
C-50606(c)

PRENTICE-HALL INTERNATIONAL, INC., London
PRENTICE-HALL OF AUSTRALIA, PTY, LTD., Sydney
PRENTICE-HALL OF CANADA, LTD., Toronto
PRENTICE-HALL OF INDIA (PRIVATE) LTD., New Delhi
PRENTICE-HALL OF JAPAN, INC., Tokyo

to Nina

Foreword

Organic chemistry today is a rapidly changing subject whose almost frenetic activity is attested by the countless research papers appearing in established and new journals and by the proliferation of monographs and reviews on all aspects of the field. This expansion of knowledge poses pedagogical problems; it is difficult for a single organic chemist to be cognizant of developments over the whole field and probably no one or pair of chemists can honestly claim expertise or even competence in all the important areas of the subject.

Yet the same rapid expansion of knowledge—in theoretical organic chemistry, in stereochemistry, in reaction mechanisms, in complex organic structures, in the application of physical methods—provides a remarkable opportunity for the teacher of organic chemistry to present the subject as it really is, an active field of research in which new answers are currently being sought and found.

To take advantage of recent developments in organic chemistry and to provide an authoritative treatment of the subject at an undergraduate level, the *Foundations of Modern Organic Chemistry Series* has been established. The series consists of a number of short, authoritative books, each written at an elementary level but in depth by an organic chemistry teacher active in research and familiar with the subject of the volume. Most of the authors have published research papers in the fields on which they are writing. The books will present the topics according to current knowledge of the field, and individual volumes will be revised as often as necessary to take account of subsequent developments.

The basic organization of the series is according to reaction type, rather than along the more classical lines of compound class. The first ten volumes in the series constitute a core of the material covered in nearly every one-year organic chemistry course. Of these ten, the first three are a general introduction to organic chemistry and provide a background for the next six, which deal with specific types of reactions and may be covered in any order. Each of the reaction types is presented from an elementary viewpoint, but in a depth not possible in conventional textbooks. The teacher can decide how much of a volume to cover. The tenth examines the problem of organic synthesis, employing and tying together the reactions previously studied.

The remaining volumes provide for the enormous flexibility of the series. These cover topics which are important to students of organic chemistry and are sometimes treated in the first organic course, sometimes in an intermediate course. Some teachers will wish to cover a number of these books in the one-year course; others will wish to assign some of them as outside reading; a complete intermediate organic course could be based on the eight "topics" texts taken together.

The series approach to undergraduate organic chemistry offers then the considerable advantage of an authoritative treatment by teachers active in research, of frequent revision of the most active areas, of a treatment in depth of the most fundamental material, and of nearly complete flexibility in choice of topics to be covered. Individually the volumes of the Foundations of Modern Organic Chemistry provide introductions in depth to basic areas of organic chemistry; together they comprise a contemporary survey of organic chemistry at an undergraduate level.

KENNETH L. RINEHART, JR.

University of Illinois

Contents

1

INTRODUCTION   1

2

ADDITIONS TO SIMPLE
ALKENES AND ALKYNES   10

NUCLEOPHILIC SUBSTITUTION   31

ELIMINATION REACTIONS   55

SUBSTITUTION VS. ELIMINATION   77

EFFECT OF UNSATURATED SUBSTITUENTS
AND OF CONJUGATION   83

ORGANOMETALLIC COMPOUNDS AND
ELECTROPHILIC ALIPHATIC SUBSTITUTION   96

SUGGESTED FURTHER READINGS   109

INDEX   111

1
Introduction

1.1 GENERAL

In any scientific textbook, a great many words and ideas that are not in common knowledge must be used. This chapter aims at familiarizing the reader with this necessary background material. Some or all of it will have been encountered by a person with any prior knowledge of organic and/or physical chemistry. Much of it is covered elsewhere in the *Foundations of Modern Organic Chemistry* series.† It is given here in the hope that the need for reference to other volumes of the series may be minimized, and major sources of confusion anticipated.

1.2 REACTION TYPES

Most textbooks of organic chemistry are organized in terms of *functional groups,* or classes, of organic compounds. The hydrocarbons occupy one chapter, the alkyl halides another, the alcohols yet another, and so on. A way of classifying our knowledge of organic reactions that has become increasingly popular in recent years uses *reaction types.* This approach considers the kinds of bonds that are formed and/or broken in the reaction. In this book, we will concentrate on three simple reaction types that are very widespread and very important: addition, substitution and elimination. These can be represented by the following general equations:

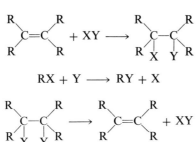

addition:

substitution: RX + Y ⟶ RY + X

elimination:

---

† Mainly in Norman L. Allinger and Janet Allinger, *The Structures of Organic Molecules* (Englewood Cliffs, N.J.: Prentice-Hall, Inc., 1965), and Ross Stewart, *Investigation of Organic Reactions* (Englewood Cliffs, N.J.: Prentice-Hall, Inc., 1965). (To be published.)

The R's represent alkyl groups (CH_3, C_2H_5, etc.) and the X's and Y's can be any of a large number of atoms or groups of atoms. The class of organic compounds into which a reactant or product falls depends on the nature of X and Y. Only in the addition reaction have we deliberately restricted ourselves to a particular functional group, the carbon-carbon double bond. Addition reactions occur with other types of double bonds, but the subject is so broad that it must be subdivided. The other important category, additions to carbon-oxygen double bonds, is treated in another volume of this series.†

1.3 REACTION MECHANISMS AND RATES

While the reaction type forms a useful basis for classifying reactions, it tells us nothing about the details of how the reaction occurs. In an addition reaction, for example, do X and Y become attached to their carbon atoms simultaneously, or in steps? If the second possibility is true, does X or Y become attached first? When we answer such questions, we are describing the *mechanism* of the reaction. If we know the mechanism, we can often predict the effect of changes in structure of reactants or in reaction conditions on the rate of the reaction. Without such knowledge, the best we can do is to discover empirical rules and apply them without knowing why they work.

A number of concepts must be kept in mind in discussing reaction mechanisms. The *rate* of a reaction is the speed with which the reactant disappears or the product appears. The rate of

$$A \longrightarrow B$$

might be expressed as the number of moles of A that react in a given time, for example. In most reactions, this rate is proportional to the amount of reactant. We might, for example, express the rate of the above reaction by the equation

$$\text{rate} = k[A]$$

Here, and elsewhere in the book, the brackets signify "concentration of." The symbol k is a proportionality constant known as the *rate constant*, and may be thought of as the rate of reaction when the reactant (or reactants) is at unit concentration. The equation expressing the dependence of rate on concentration is the *rate law* for the particular reaction.

While the rate law given is a probable one for the conversion of A to B, it is by no means the only possibility. Suppose *two* molecules of A must

† Carl D. Gutsche, *The Chemistry of Carbonyl Compounds* (Englewood Cliffs, N.J.: Prentice-Hall, Inc., 1965). (To be published.)

collide with each other to produce B. The rate law then would be

$$\text{rate} = k'[\text{A}][\text{A}] = k'[\text{A}]^2$$

Therefore, the *order* of reaction must be considered. The reaction just shown depends on the second power of the concentration of A and is *second order*. The earlier example is *first order*. Another possible mechanism might involve collision of A with a catalyst C before reaction could occur. The rate law corresponding to this situation is

$$\text{rate} = k''[\text{A}][\text{C}]$$

and the reaction is second order overall, first order in A, and first order in C.

The possibilities are still not exhausted, for the conversion of A to B might occur in more than one step. Suppose A is first converted to an *intermediate* X, which then goes on to B:

$$\text{A} \longrightarrow \text{X} \longrightarrow \text{B}$$

Usually one of these steps will be slower than the other, and is called the *rate-determining step*. If A is converted slowly to X, and X rapidly to B, the reaction can go no faster than the first step. Adding a catalyst that would make X go to B ten times faster would not increase the speed at which B is formed, for the rate of formation of X constitutes a "bottleneck" that limits the rate of the overall reaction. If the first step is fast and the second slow, then the concentration of X will build up in the reaction mixture, and again B can form no faster than the slower (here, the second) step.

This concept enables us to discuss more thoroughly the relationship between the mechanism and the rate law. Obviously, the rate law for the overall reaction must express the rate of the rate-determining step. Let us assume a still more complex mechanism in which A goes to an intermediate X, which then reacts with another substance, C:

$$\text{A} \longrightarrow \text{X}$$

$$\text{X} + \text{C} \longrightarrow \text{B}$$

If the first step is the slow one, then the formation of B cannot be hurried by adding more C, and the rate law is

$$\text{rate} = k_1[\text{A}]$$

That is, the rate is independent of the concentration of C even though C is an essential reactant and the overall reaction is

$$\text{A} + \text{C} \longrightarrow \text{B}$$

We can state generally that any reactant which enters into reaction after the rate-determining step will not appear in the rate law.

If the second step of our example is slow, then the rate depends on C:

$$\text{rate} = k_2[\text{X}][\text{C}]$$

This expression is not very useful as it stands, because X is an intermediate whose concentration we do not know. If A is in *equilibrium* with X,

$$K = \frac{[\text{X}]}{[\text{A}]}$$

and

$$[\text{X}] = K[\text{A}]$$

so that

$$\text{rate} = k_2 K[\text{A}][\text{C}]$$

and the rate law is of precisely the same form as it would be if A reacted directly with C to give B without any intermediate. This will be true only if the equilibrium is established much faster than X is used up in the second step. When it is not, the rate law can become rather complicated. Knowledge of these more complicated situations is not necessary for an understanding of the material to follow.

It should be evident by now that the observed rate law for a reaction may be a great help in deducing the reaction mechanism. As noted above, a reactant which does not appear in the rate law cannot be involved in the rate-determining step, and this fact enables us to exclude any potential mechanisms in which it does. Also, a mechanism may be discarded because it predicts the wrong order in a particular reactant. If all conceivable mechanisms but one can be eliminated, then we have "proved" that mechanism. Often we are not so lucky, for more than one mechanism may predict the same rate law. Then we must seek sources of information other than the rate law alone. Among these are the effect on rate of changing the structure of the reactant or the nature of the solvent. How such deductions are made will be seen more clearly when specific examples are presented in subsequent chapters. The whole field of the study of rates and mechanisms of reactions, incidentally, is a branch of chemistry called *reaction kinetics*.

1.4 ACTIVATION ENERGY AND ENERGY DIAGRAMS

It is common in organic chemistry to find that a reaction does not occur unless heat is supplied. Even if the equilibrium position of the reaction is far on the side of the products, bringing the reactants together does not ensure that reaction will occur. Nearly all reactions, in fact, must surmount an energy barrier before they can occur; for some, the heat energy available at room temperature or lower suffices. This energy barrier is called the *activation energy*. The larger the activation energy, the higher the temperature must be for reaction to occur at a reasonable rate. As the temperature is raised, more and more molecules acquire enough energy to react, and the rate of reaction increases. The higher the activation energy of a reaction, the larger will be the rate increase resulting from a given temperature increase. The mathematical relationship obeyed by most reactions is

$$k = Ae^{-E_a/RT}$$

where A and R are constants, T the absolute temperature, and E_a the activation energy.

The concept of activation energy provides us with an additional way to examine reaction mechanisms. We can describe the energy of a reacting system at any time during the reaction by a graph with energy plotted on the y axis and the extent of reaction (the "reaction coordinate") along the x axis. (Actually, the quantity plotted is what is called the "free energy" in thermodynamics, but we need not make the distinction for purposes of our present discussion.) Such a plot for a simple one-step reaction is shown in Fig. 1. The point labeled I represents reactants, II the *transition state*, and III the products.

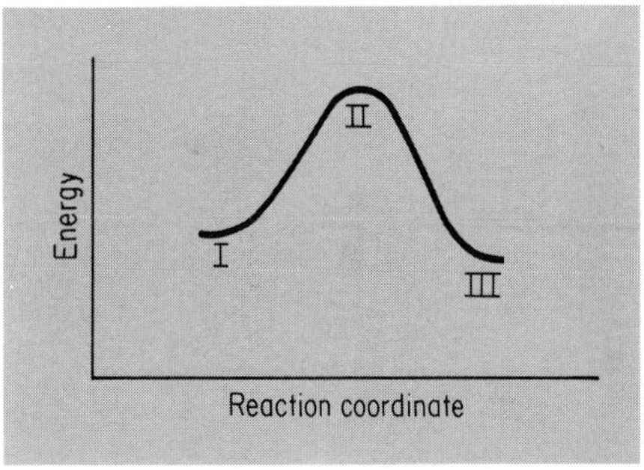

A clear idea of what II represents is essential to an understanding of reaction mechanisms. The *difference* in energy between II and I is the activation energy (again, the correct quantity would be the free energy of activation), and determines the rate of the reaction at any given temperature. We can thus discuss the effects of other variables (solvent, structure of reactant, nature of attacking reagent, etc.) in terms of how they affect this energy

Fig. 1

difference. If a change in solvent stabilizes the transition state more than it does the reactants, it will accelerate the reaction. Note that the *difference* is the important factor. If a given change has the same effect on the energy of the reactant as it does on the energy of the transition state, there will be no change in rate.

Often we say that one reaction goes faster than another because its product is more stable. This is an inexact way of speaking, for the energy of the product has no necessary relation to the energies of either reactant or transition state. Such an approach is useful, however, because the transition state exists somewhere on the reaction coordinate between reactant and product, and may have some of the characteristics of the product. The transition state is too short-lived ever to be isolated or observed, so we can never know directly what it looks like. We can observe the products, though, and determine or deduce what factors will raise or lower their energy. We should keep in mind that this approximation can and does fail when the transition state and products are not similar.

1.5 MULTISTEP REACTIONS AND UNSTABLE INTERMEDIATES

Free energy diagrams of the sort just shown can also be drawn for reactions having two or more steps. An example is shown in Fig. 2. Here I is (are) the reactant(s); II, the transition state for the first step; III, the intermediate; IV, the transition state for the second step; V, the products. This diagram could apply to our earlier example

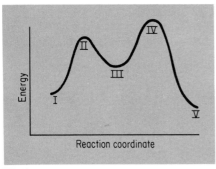

Fig. 2

$$A \longrightarrow X \longrightarrow B$$

More specifically, our diagram represents the case where the second step is rate-determining, for its transition state IV is of higher energy than II. Such a diagram would apply to the case where reactant I is in equilibrium with intermediate III. Here III is said to be an *unstable intermediate* because it cannot be isolated. It is of much higher energy than either I or V, and hence will be present in a very low concentration in the equilibrium. In addition, any effort to isolate even a small amount during reaction would be frustrated by its rapid (low activation energy) reconversion to I.

Instability is a relative matter. Suppose the "valley" in which III is located were deepened. Eventually a point would be reached at which the activation energy for the reconversion of III to I would be so high that III could be isolated as a *stable intermediate*. The exact point at which the changeover from unstable to stable occurs is indefinite, and depends mainly on the quality of our techniques for isolation.

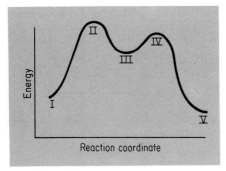

Fig. 3

A reaction whose first step is rate-determining could be represented by Fig. 3. The roman numerals have the same meanings as before. Again, III is an unstable intermediate. It will always be present in very low concentration, for its rate of formation from I is slower than its rate of conversion to V. Efforts to isolate III will again be frustrated, this time by its rapid reaction to form the product V.

We have called III an *intermediate* in both of the above examples, but we might just as well call it the *product* of the first stage of the reaction. It is a special sort of product, for it is much closer in energy to the transition state through which it was formed than products usually are. A very important generalization, *Hammond's Postulate,* states that two adjacent species along a reaction coordinate that are similar in energy will be similar in electronic structure as well. Thus, the transition state probably resembles closely the unstable intermediate that follows it (or precedes it, in the case of IV). Discussion of effects on the rate of a reaction in terms of effects on the energy of an unstable intermediate are therefore particularly likely to be justified. We will see many examples of such reasoning in later chapters.

Although we have emphasized the rates of organic reactions in our discussion so far, the success or failure of a reaction is not always determined by its rate. Many reactions are *reversible,* and attain fairly rapidly a position of equilibrium. At equilibrium, the predominant species will be that having the lowest energy (again, the proper term is "free energy"). If the reactant is more stable than the product, the reaction will not give a good yield of product no matter how long it is carried on or how strenuous the conditions. Only if there is some means of shifting the equilibrium, such as removing the product by distillation as it forms, will it be possible to get a good yield.

When a reaction does give a good yield of product, it may do so either because the equilibrium favors product, or because the product is formed at a good rate in an *irreversible* reaction. The former is a case of *equilibrium control* or *thermodynamic control.* (Thermodynamics deals with chemical and physical systems at equilibrium.) The latter is a case of *rate control* or *kinetic control.* It is important to know which type of control is operating in a particular reaction, for efforts to improve the yield may call for entirely different measures in the two cases.

Changing the reaction conditions can sometimes cause a changeover from one type of control to another. Suppose a reactant A can give rapidly and reversibly a product B, and slowly and irreversibly another product C:

$$A \underset{}{\overset{\text{fast}}{\rightleftharpoons}} B$$
$$\downarrow \text{slow}$$
$$C$$

If the reaction is run for a short time, or at low temperature, the major product is B, but for a longer time or at higher temperatures the major product is C. As A goes irreversibly to C, the equilibrium shifts to the left and all of the first-formed B is converted to C via A.

1.6 ELECTRONIC STRUCTURES OF MOLECULES AND INTERMEDIATES

So far we have talked about unstable intermediates in a general sense only. It will be useful now to consider what types of unstable intermediates are common in organic reactions and how they are formed. We will take as our example a covalent organic compound CH_3X and discuss the various ways in which it can be broken up. In this compound, carbon has eight electrons in its outer shell and is electrically neutral; i.e., it bears no net charge. Two electrons are shared with each of three hydrogens, and the remaining two are shared with X. One electron of each of these pairs can be regarded as "belonging" to carbon, so that the carbon atom's share totals four electrons, which is the same as that of an isolated carbon atom.

There are two main ways in which the CH_3—X bond could break. The first is *homolytic,* in which one electron of the bond goes to carbon and one to X:

$$CH_3{:}X \longrightarrow CH_3{\cdot} + X{\cdot}$$

Now, the carbon is still electrically neutral, because it shares six electrons with the three hydrogens, of which three "belong" to it, and it has one unshared electron of its own for a total of four. Yet the outer shell of carbon in this species is electron deficient, for it contains only seven electrons when it could hold eight. Its electronic structure is

$$\begin{array}{c} H \\ \overset{\cdot\cdot}{H{:}\underset{\cdot\cdot}{C}}{\cdot} \\ H \end{array}$$

Such a species with an odd number of electrons is called a *free radical.* The above example is a methyl radical.

We will give little attention to free-radical intermediates in this volume. Our main interest will be in the two remaining ways in which the CH_3—X bond can break. These involve both electrons of the bond going to one or the other of the two groups, a process called *heterolytic* cleavage.

If both electrons of the bond go to X, the carbon atom loses two electrons from its outer shell and thus has only six electrons. It now "owns" only its share of the six; that is, three. Since this is one electron less than the normal complement of four, the methyl group now bears a positive charge, and is called a *carbonium ion.* Its electronic structure is

Almost all carbonium ions are so unstable that they cannot be observed directly. Their presence as intermediates in certain reactions is inferred in a way that we will see later. All three of the major reaction types discussed in this volume—addition, substitution and elimination—can proceed by mechanisms involving carbonium ions.

The remaining way in which the CH_3X bond can split is for both electrons to go to the methyl group. The resulting species is

$$\begin{array}{c} H \\ \overset{\cdot\cdot}{H{:}\underset{\cdot\cdot}{C}}{:}{-} \\ H \end{array}$$

It is called a *carbanion,* and is negatively charged because the carbon "owns" one more electron than a neutral carbon atom (its share of three electrons in the C—H bonds, plus the two unshared electrons). The carbon has a full complement of eight electrons in its outer shell. Its reactions, consequently, are with electron-deficient species in contrast to the carbonium ion, which reacts with electron-rich species.

The descriptions of the important intermediates in organic reactions are given above in some detail because they are very important to the material of later chapters. Other aspects of electronic structure will only be mentioned here, as they are covered thoroughly in N. L. Allinger, *op. cit.*

The student should be familiar with the various types of bonding to carbon atoms, specifically the sp^3 orbitals of saturated carbon, the sp^2 orbitals of doubly-bonded carbon, and the sp orbitals of triply-bonded carbon. He should also know the nature of unhybridized s and p orbitals, and the ways in which all of these types of *atomic orbitals* overlap to give σ and π molecular orbitals. Included in this knowledge should be a description of the bond angles found with sp^3, sp^2 and sp bonds. The conditions under which a molecule may exist as a resonance hybrid of two or more possible structures, and the effect of resonance on stability should be thoroughly understood. Stereochemistry, including optical activity, *cis-trans* isomerism, and conformational analysis will be used extensively.

CHAPTER 1 REVIEW QUESTIONS

1. Define the following: functional group, mechanism, rate constant, rate-determining step, activation energy.

2. State the differences between the two members of each of the following pairs of terms: transition state and unstable intermediate, thermodynamic and kinetic control.

3. Show the arrangement of the electrons in the outer shell of a free radical, a carbanion and a carbonium ion. Explain why the last two are charged and the first is not.

4. The rate of reaction of acetone with bromine,

$$CH_3COCH_3 + Br_2 \longrightarrow CH_3COCH_2Br + HBr$$

is independent of bromine concentration. What type of mechanism does this indicate? Draw an energy diagram that would apply here.

5. 3-Phenylpropene is converted to 1-phenylpropene on treatment with strong base at high temperatures. What can you say about the relative free energies of the two compounds?

2
Additions to Simple Alkenes and Alkynes

2.1 GENERAL

Additions to double or triple bonds occur in a very large number of organic reactions. Many of these are simple additions, and many more are preceded or followed by other steps. The multiple bond may exist between almost any two atoms capable of forming multiple bonds. In organic chemistry, carbon-carbon, carbon-oxygen and carbon-nitrogen multiple bonds are of particular interest. This chapter will be limited to addition reactions of carbon-carbon double and triple bonds. Most of the reactions we will discuss involve addition of an *electrophilic* (electron deficient) reagent.

2.2 SOME EXAMPLES OF ADDITION REACTIONS

In addition reactions of olefins, the π orbital is destroyed, and two new σ bonds are formed to the two parts of the addend:

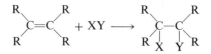

Prominent examples are the addition of halogens and halogen acids to olefins:

$$CH_2{=}CH_2 + Br_2 \longrightarrow BrCH_2CH_2Br$$

$$CH_2{=}CH_2 + HBr \longrightarrow CH_3CH_2Br$$

In each case one part of the addend goes to one carbon atom and the other part goes to the other. Usually there is no problem in predicting the two parts the addend will break into. There is no choice with Br_2 and HBr, and even in more complicated addends the break usually occurs where one would expect it; for example, between H and OSO_3H in sulfuric acid. Very weak acids may not always add as expected. The addition of HOCl to ethylene goes according to the equation

$$CH_2{=}CH_2 + HOCl \longrightarrow HOCH_2CH_2Cl$$

The break is between HO and Cl rather than between H and OCl.

2.3 MECHANISM OF HALOGEN ADDITION TO OLEFINS

The natural question to ask next is whether the two parts of the addend become attached simultaneously, or in stepwise fashion. Nearly all of the additions that we shall discuss in this chapter appear to be stepwise processes. Before we detail what is believed to happen in halogen additions, we shall consider an illuminating piece of evidence. The addition of bromine to ethylene normally gives 1,2-dibromoethane, but in the presence of sodium chloride or of sodium nitrate it can give different products:

$$CH_2\text{=}CH_2 + Br_2 \begin{array}{l} \longrightarrow BrCH_2CH_2Br \\ \xrightarrow{NaCl} BrCH_2CH_2Cl \\ \xrightarrow{NaNO_3} BrCH_2CH_2ONO_2 \end{array}$$

The bromine clearly cannot be adding all at once, for in that case the salts could not take part in the reaction. Since these added substances provide *anions* that enter into the reaction, the course of the reaction is probably:

$$CH_2\text{=}CH_2 + Br_2 \longrightarrow BrCH_2CH_2^+ + Br^-$$

$$BrCH_2CH_2^+ \left\{ \begin{array}{l} \xrightarrow{Cl^-} BrCH_2CH_2Cl \\ \xrightarrow{Br^-} BrCH_2CH_2Br \end{array} \right.$$

The addition can be thought of as a heterolytic cleavage of bromine to give Br^+ and Br^-, followed by reaction of the Br^+ with the double bond:

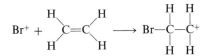

The electrons that were originally in the π orbital form a bond to the electron-deficient Br^+. The other carbon atom is thus deprived altogether of the electron pair that it had shared and becomes a *carbonium ion*. The carbonium ion satisfies its electron deficiency by reacting rapidly with an anion, which can supply the electron pair needed to form a new bond. The intermediate carbonium ion reacts as soon as it is formed, and thus never accumulates in sufficient concentration to be observed or isolated.

The question of whether the Br^+ ion or, with halogens in general, the X^+ ion is a real intermediate in the reaction cannot be given a simple answer. The kinetics of the reaction is not of much help, as the rate is given by

$$\text{rate} = k[\text{olefin}][X_2]$$

This could mean a direct attack of X_2 on the olefin in which a free X^+ is never involved, and in which the carbonium ion and X^- ion are formed directly. The rate law is also consistent, unfortunately, with a mechanism in which the X^+ ion is in equilibrium with the free halogen. The X^+ concentration would be proportional to the concentration of halogen, and the rate would still depend on the first power of the halogen concentration.

In some cases, as in bromination in acetic acid, a more complex rate law results:

$$\text{rate} = k[\text{olefin}][\text{Br}_2]^2$$

Here *two* molecules of Br_2 must be present in the rate-determining step. The most probable mechanism for these conditions involves attack by molecular bromine, with the second bromine molecule helping to remove Br^- as the Br_3^- complex ion. The net result is transfer of Br^+ to the olefin, but there is never any free Br^+ present. The electron shifts that occur in this process are

$$CH_2{=}CH_2 \quad Br{-}Br \quad Br{-}Br \longrightarrow {}^+CH_2CH_2Br + Br_3^-$$

Each arrow represents the movement of an electron pair in the direction indicated. It is likely that most, if not all, halogen additions involve either molecular halogen or some molecular species derived from it, such as HOX, and not a free X^+ ion. Presumably, the solvent helps the removal of X^- during the addition in those reactions where only a single halogen molecule is present in the transition state.

The mechanism for halogen addition given so far is not complete, for it does not account for an important feature of the reaction—its stereochemistry. This point can be illustrated by the addition of bromine to butenedioic acid. Because free rotation about the double bond is impossible, it exists as two isomers known by the trivial names of maleic (*cis*) and fumaric (*trans*) acids. The dibromides obtained from these two acids are structurally the same, but they are two different *diastereomers*, one called a ($\pm$) and the other called *meso*. The addition therefore must have occurred in a specific fashion, and it turns out that the two bromine atoms add to opposite sides of the double bond.

Such specificity would not be expected from the carbonium ion intermediate postulated earlier, for both olefins would give the same carbonium ion and hence the same final product or products:

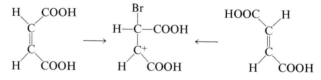

There would be free rotation about the single carbon-carbon bond of the intermediate, so that initial differences in rotational conformation would disappear rapidly. Direct, one-stage addition of a bromine molecule is excluded both by the results mentioned earlier, and by the fact that the two bromine atoms add *trans* rather than *cis*.

Rotation in the intermediate may be avoided, and the correct *trans* mode of addition obtained, if the initial step leads to attachment of the Br^+ to *both* carbon atoms of the double bond. The subsequent attack by Br^- must then be from the other side. Addition of bromine to maleic acid by this mechanism follows the sequence:

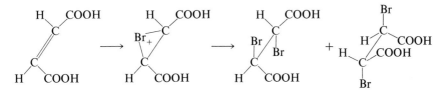

The two products, obtained by attack of bromine at either of the two carbons of the intermediate, are mirror images of each other and, hence, are *enantiomers,* or a ± pair. Fumaric acid, on the other hand, yields a single product:

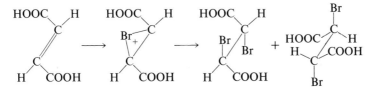

The "two" products may be seen to be identical by rotating both of them so that the bromine atoms are eclipsed. This is the *meso* isomer, and is diastereomeric with the ± pair.

The intermediate we have postulated is called a *bromonium ion.* It enables us to account for all of the facts about halogen addition presented up to this point. Its formation can be thought of as involving initial association of the electron-deficient Br^+ with one lobe of the π orbital, in the same manner as in formation of a π complex. Probably, the bonding of bromine to the two carbons in the bromonium ion is stronger than that in a simple π complex, as some energy must be gained in the formation of bonds between bromine and carbon to offset that needed to break the bromine-bromine bond of Br_2. The exact nature of the bonding remains uncertain because the bromonium ion is too unstable to isolate or observe. Most halogen additions are *trans* and presumably involve "halonium" ion intermediates. Some violations of the rule are known for chlorine additions. Apparently the chloronium ion, at least under certain circumstances, is less stable than a simple β-chlorocarbonium ion.

2.4 MECHANISMS OF THE REACTIONS OF OLEFINS
WITH UNSYMMETRICAL ADDENDS

Many additions of unsymmetrical addends appear to proceed via halonium ion intermediates. The byproducts of the bromine-ethylene reaction obtained in the presence of added salts (see above) result from the attack of chloride or nitrate ions on the bromonium ion. Acid-catalyzed addition of hypohalous acids to olefins seems to follow the mechanism:

$$HOX + H^+ \rightleftharpoons H_2OX^+$$

$$H_2OX^+ + CH_2{=}CH_2 \longrightarrow \underset{CH_2{-}CH_2}{\overset{X}{\triangle}}{}^+ + H_2O$$

$$\underset{CH_2{-}CH_2}{\overset{X}{\triangle}}{}^+ + H_2O \longrightarrow XCH_2CH_2OH$$

Another class of unsymmetrical addends are the interhalogen compounds such as ICl:

$$ICl + CH_2{=}CH_2 \longrightarrow \underset{CH_2{-}CH_2}{\overset{I}{\triangle}}{}^+ + Cl^-$$

$$\underset{CH_2{-}CH_2}{\overset{I}{\triangle}}{}^+ + Cl^- \longrightarrow ICH_2CH_2Cl$$

The most common type of unsymmetrical addend has the formula HX. Reaction is initiated by protonation of the olefin, and completed by combination of the carbonium ion with the nucleophilic portion of the addend, X:

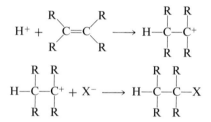

Among the many examples are the acid-catalyzed addition of water to give alcohols, of hydrohalic acids to give alkyl halides, and of sulfuric acid to give alkyl sulfates.

At least some of these additions have been considered to involve formation of a π complex between the proton and the olefin, prior to formation of the carbonium ion:

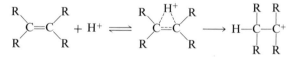

Most of the evidence for this picture was of a rather indirect nature, involving some fairly complex deductions from the dependence of rate on the acidity of the medium, and on the deuterium content in mixtures of water and heavy water. We will not go into the matter in detail, except to mention that more recent work has cast doubt on the general validity of these deductions, and therefore on the necessity for assuming an intermediate π complex.

In the case of halogen addition, a study of the stereochemistry of the reaction allowed a distinction to be drawn between an open carbonium ion and a cyclic halonium ion intermediate. Less work has been done on the addition of HX. What evidence there is indicates that some reactions are stereospecific and others not. Hydration of 1,2-dimethylcyclohexene gives both *cis* and *trans* product, while addition of HBr to the same olefin gives only *trans* product:

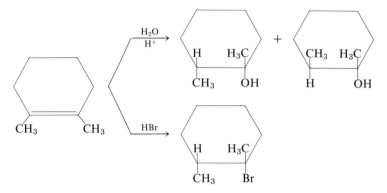

The first reaction is carried out in water, which is very effective for solvating ions. The open carbonium ion thus might be expected to form fairly easily. The second reaction is carried out in glacial acetic acid, which is a less effective ion-solvating medium. The attack of bromide ion may be on a π complex or a similar symmetrically-protonated intermediate. In either case, the charge would be spread over three atoms instead of being concentrated on one, and less solvation should be required:†

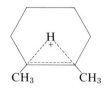

The postulated intermediate may, as indicated, have the proton more tightly bound than in a simple π complex. In this respect, it is similar to the bromonium ion, though hydrogen cannot form more than one full covalent bond at a time.

Recent work has even provided evidence for a mechanism that gives predominantly *cis* addition. For example:†

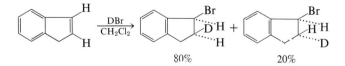

† In these formulas and elsewhere, a *dashed* line means a partial bond; a *dotted* line means a bond which projects back into the plane of the paper.

The D stands for deuterium, the heavy isotope of hydrogen, which is used to distinguish between the otherwise identical products of *cis* and *trans* addition. Dewar† suggests that the DBr donates D^+ to the olefin to form a carbonium ion, and that the Br^- from the DBr remains close to the carbonium ion on the same side of the molecule to which the D^+ added. The result is an *ion pair* which reacts to give *cis* addend. The small amount of *trans* addend might result from some ion pairs diffusing apart. The generality of *cis* addition remains uncertain, as all examples so far have an aromatic ring attached to the double bond.

The dependence of rate of reaction on concentrations of reactants in additions of HX is more or less as expected for the mechanism given. The slow step is the initial attack of a proton, or proton-donating species, on the olefin. The rate law for hydration is

$$\text{rate} = k[\text{olefin}][H_3O^+]$$

in dilute acid solution. In strong acid the rate increases faster than $[H_3O^+]$ does. Experimentally, the rate parallels the ability of the acid medium to donate a proton to a base. This criterion of acidity is called the *Hammett* ‡ *Acidity Function* (H_0), and is measured by using basic indicators of known ionization constants. The detailed mechanistic implications of dependence of rate on H_0 are still subject to dispute, and will not be discussed here. There does not seem to be any reason to believe that the mechanism is fundamentally different from that described at the beginning of the paragraph.

Some kinetic complications are encountered in the addition of hydrogen halides to olefins in non-polar solvents. In heptane, for example, the rate law is approximately

$$\text{rate} = k[\text{olefin}][HX]^3$$

The two "extra" molecules of HX are believed to be necessary simply to solvate the transition state. The solvent, heptane, is very inefficient at solvating charged species. This unexpectedly complicated rate law points up a difficulty often encountered in studying kinetics in inert solvents. The solvent may make polar reactants form dimeric or polymeric associated species, and may, as in this case, force a reactant to fill a role normally played by solvent. For these reasons, attempts to "simplify" the study of ionic reactions by using inert solvents often result in increased complication.

† M. J. S. Dewar. Born 1918. English by birth; now at the University of Texas. Formerly at the University of Chicago and Queen Mary College, London. Theoretical organic chemistry, especially the application of quantum mechanics to organic chemistry.

‡ L. P. Hammett. Born 1894. American. Columbia University. Important work on substituent effects (the Hammett equation) and on solutions of strong acids. Author of a very influential text, *Physical Organic Chemistry* (New York: McGraw-Hill Book Co., Inc., 1940).

2.5 RELATIVE REACTIVITIES AND ORIENTATION IN ADDITIONS

With the mechanisms of these addition reactions in mind, prediction of the effect of structure on reactivity is easy. Since the slow step is the attack of a positively-charged and/or electron-deficient species on the double bond, electron-repelling substituents should aid reaction by increasing electron density at the double bond. A typical sequence of reactivities is

$$CH_2{=}CH_2 < RCH{=}CH_2 < R_2C{=}CH_2 < R_2C{=}CHR < R_2C{=}CR_2$$

Here R is any alkyl group. Substitution of halogens or other electron-withdrawing groups on the double bond decreases reactivity. Vinyl bromide, for example, is less reactive than ethylene. Certain unsaturated groups, such as phenyl (C_6H_5), increase reactivity greatly, for reasons that will be discussed in Chap. 5.

A special case of relative reactivities occurs in the addition of unsymmetrical addends (HX, HOX, etc.) to unsymmetrical olefins. In principle, the addition could occur in either of two ways to give two products, but in practice only one is usually obtained. Addition of HBr to propylene, for example, gives only isopropyl bromide:

$$CH_3CH{=}CH_2 + HBr \nearrow \begin{array}{c} CH_3CHCH_3 \\ | \\ Br \end{array} \text{(sole product)}$$

$$\searrow CH_3CH_2CH_2Br \text{ (not formed)}$$

This is an example of addition according to the *Markovnikov†* Rule. As originally stated, it said that addition of HX to unsymmetrical olefins always occurs so that X becomes attached to that carbon atom (of the double bond) bearing the lesser number of hydrogens (or the greater number of alkyl groups) and H becomes attached to that carbon atom bearing the greater number of hydrogens.

In mechanistic terms, addition of a proton in each of the two possible directions would give two different intermediate carbonium ions:

$$CH_3CH{=}CH_2 + H^+ \nearrow CH_3CH_2CH_2^+$$
$$\searrow CH_3\overset{+}{C}HCH_3$$

† V. V. Markovnikov, 1838–1904. Russian. Director of the Chemical Institute of the University of Moscow. The chemistry of hydrocarbons and the effect of structure on the course of reaction. The original Russian spelling of his name is Марковников, which has been rendered into various English versions. The most frequently encountered are Markownikoff and the version given above.

The first of these is a *primary* carbonium ion, which has a single alkyl (ethyl) group attached to the electron-deficient carbon atom. The other is a *secondary* carbonium ion, which has two alkyl (methyl) groups attached to the electron-deficient carbon atom. Because they are electron repelling, alkyl groups help to stabilize the carbonium ion, and two of them are better than one. The more stable carbonium ion is formed preferentially, and it leads to the Markovnikov-rule product, isopropyl bromide. In general, the carbonium ion having the most alkyl groups attached to the electron-deficient carbon atom is favored. We have seen in Chap. 1 the justification for assuming that a more stable intermediate will form more rapidly.

A knowledge of the mechanisms of addition reactions enables us to predict the direction of addition in many cases not covered by the original Markovnikov rule. The addition of hypochlorous acid to propylene, for example, clearly follows the path

$$CH_3CH{=}CH_2 \xrightarrow{Cl^+} CH_3\underset{+}{CH}{-}\underset{|}{\underset{Cl}{CH_2}} \xrightarrow{H_2O} CH_3\underset{|}{\underset{OH}{CH}}{-}\underset{|}{\underset{Cl}{CH_2}}$$

The alternate mode of addition would involve a primary carbonium ion.

Similarly, we can deal with olefins bearing substituents other than alkyl groups. Addition of halogen acids to vinyl halides gives ethylidene halides:

$$CH_2{=}CHCl + HCl \longrightarrow CH_3CHCl_2$$

The unshared electrons on the halogen help to stabilize the carbonium ion by resonance:

$$CH_3{-}\overset{+}{C}H{-}\overset{..}{\underset{..}{C}}l{:} \longleftrightarrow CH_3{-}CH{=}\overset{+}{\underset{..}{C}}l{:}$$

Strongly electron-withdrawing groups destabilize a carbonium ion and therefore induce "anti-Markovnikov" addition:

$$[CH_3]_3\overset{+}{N}CH{=}CH_2 + HI \longrightarrow [CH_3]_3\overset{+}{N}CH_2CH_2I$$

Addition of a proton to the end carbon would lead to positive charges on adjacent atoms. The examples in this and the preceding paragraph provide good illustrations of the superiority of mechanistic reasoning over empirical rules.

Under most conditions, the Markovnikov rule is obeyed very strictly. In additions to simple olefins, no detectable yields of "anti-Markovnikov" products are normally produced. Seldom is so highly specific a preference noted for one of two or more possible paths in organic chemistry.

This high specificity was not always apparent, for there existed in the literature numerous puzzling reports of anti-Markovnikov additions of hydrogen bromide. Often the same olefin was found by different workers, or even by the same worker at different times, to yield products having different orientations. This puzzling state of affairs was finally cleared up by Kharasch† and Mayo in 1933. They showed that the anti-Markovnikov additions resulted from the operation of a different mechanism.

Their experimental observations were as follows: First, addition of hydrogen bromide to allyl bromide without any special precautions yielded the abnormal product:

$$CH_2{=}CHCH_2Br + HBr \longrightarrow BrCH_2CH_2CH_2Br$$

If however, the reactants were very carefully purified, and the reaction performed in the absence of air, normal addition occurred:

$$CH_2{=}CHCH_2Br + HBr \longrightarrow CH_3\underset{\underset{\displaystyle Br}{|}}{C}HCH_2Br$$

The key observation was that even these very pure reactants gave abnormal product if a small amount of an organic peroxide was added. Peroxide must have been responsible for the abnormal results in the first experiment, too, for olefins (among other organic compounds) are known to form peroxides on prolonged exposure to oxygen.

These observations led Kharasch and Mayo to suspect that the reaction involved *free radicals* as intermediates, for peroxides are known to form radicals easily. Other characteristics of radical reactions were also noted. The mechanism they suggested involved generation of radicals from the peroxide as the first step. The exact nature of the radicals depends on the peroxide. One possibility is:

$$ROOR \longrightarrow 2RO{\cdot}$$

Here the oxygen-oxygen bond has cleaved so that one electron of the bond goes to each of the two RO· radicals, each of which now has an oxygen with only seven electrons in its outer shell. (For convenience, we usually write only the odd electron. The correct formula is, of course, R:Ö·. In all cases, the single dot on any atom implies an outer shell of *seven* electrons.) In order to complete its octet, RO· abstracts a hydrogen atom from HBr, thereby leaving a bromine atom. Each step creates a new radical, and the complete sequence is:

$$RO{\cdot} + HBr \longrightarrow ROH + Br{\cdot}$$

$$Br{\cdot} + CH_2{=}CHCH_2Br \longrightarrow BrCH_2\overset{\displaystyle \cdot}{C}HCH_2Br$$

$$BrCH_2\overset{\displaystyle \cdot}{C}HCH_2Br + HBr \longrightarrow BrCH_2CH_2CH_2Br + Br{\cdot}$$

† M. S. Kharasch, 1895–1958. American. Professor of Organic Chemistry at the University of Chicago. Formation and reactions of free radicals, Grignard reagents, and the relation between structure and reactivity.

Addition of Br· to the olefin occurs in the direction shown because a secondary is preferred to a primary radical. The reason is probably similar to that for the analogous preference for secondary carbonium ions— the radical is also electron-deficient, even though it is not charged. Because it is now bromine that adds first, rather than hydrogen as in the ionic addition, a reversal of orientation results.

The need for only small amounts of peroxide is also apparent. The last step generates a bromine atom, which can add to another molecule of olefin, and the addition can keep repeating itself until something happens to destroy a radical (usually combination with another radical to give a stable molecule). Such a self-sustaining process is called a *chain reaction*. Each radical from the peroxide produces ultimately many molecules of addition product.

Many other additions to olefins can occur via free-radical mechanisms. Particularly noteworthy is *polymerization,* or the joining together of many molecules of olefin to form the giant molecules that make up plastics. We will not consider these reactions further as they are dealt with elsewhere in this series†, and our major concern is ionic addition.

2.6 MECHANISMS OF ADDITIONS TO ACETYLENES

The acetylenes are fundamentally very similar to the olefins in structure. The triple bond consists of a σ orbital plus a cylindrical π orbital containing four electrons.

The π electrons are, as in olefins, more exposed to attack than the σ electrons, and ionic additions are therefore usually initiated by attack of an electron-deficient species on these electrons. Acetylenes undergo many of the same addition reactions as olefins. Much of what we have said about mechanism and stereochemistry of additions to olefins applies also in additions to acetylenes.

Acetylenes are usually less reactive than olefins in addition reactions. The reasons for this phenomenon are not known with certainty, but a plausible explanation runs as follows. If the addition mechanisms are analogous to those for olefins, the first (rate determining) step will give an intermediate having a structure like one of the following:

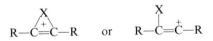

In the first intermediate the C=C—X bond angles are held to approximately 60°, while they would be 120° in a normal open-chain structure. Clearly, this intermediate is under more bond-angle strain than its satu-

† William A. Pryor, *Introduction to Free Radical Chemistry* (Englewood Cliffs, N.J.: Prentice-Hall, Inc., 1965). (To be published.)

rated counterpart, where a deformation from only 109°28' to 60° is required. The second (acyclic) intermediate is also expected to be less stable than its saturated counterpart, for somewhat subtler reasons. The electrons in s orbitals are much closer to the atom, on the average, than those in p orbitals. Therefore, the affinity for electrons of an atom with hybrid orbitals increases with the s *character* of the orbital, giving the sequence $sp^3 < sp^2 < sp$. The second intermediate has a positive charge on an sp carbon atom, and the greater electron affinity of this atom makes it less capable than an sp^2 carbon atom of bearing electron deficiency.

Aside from the overall lesser reactivity, acetylenes follow a pattern analogous to that of olefins. Electron-repelling substituents (mainly alkyl) increase, and electron-withdrawing substituents decrease, reactivity. The Markovnikov rule applies here as well:

$$R-C{\equiv}CH + HX \longrightarrow R-\overset{X}{\underset{|}{C}}=CH_2$$

The product is still unsaturated and can add a second molecule of HX. It will add in the same direction as the first, for reasons outlined in describing additions to vinyl halides:

$$R-\overset{X}{\underset{|}{C}}=CH_2 + HX \longrightarrow R-\overset{X}{\underset{\underset{X}{|}}{\overset{|}{C}}}-CH_3$$

Finally, the stereochemistry of addition to triple bonds also seems to parallel that in additions to olefins. Addition of halogen acids to acetylenedicarboxylic acid, for example, yields mainly the *trans* product:

$$HOOC-C{\equiv}C-COOH + HX \longrightarrow \underset{HOOC}{\overset{H}{}}C=C\overset{COOH}{\underset{X}{}}$$

2.7 SYNTHETIC APPLICATIONS OF ADDITION REACTIONS

Only a few addition reactions of unsaturated compounds have been cited while discussing mechanism, reactivity and stereochemistry. In fact, a large number of different organic compounds can be synthesized from olefins. We will consider the more important addition reactions and their applications in organic synthesis in the following pages.

Addition of halogens to double bonds gives 1,2-dihalides, which are useful as organic solvents. A particularly important example is 1,2-dichloroethane (often called ethylene dichloride) from chlorine and ethylene. Addition of a solution of bromine in carbon tetrachloride to a compound suspected of unsaturation is a common test for olefins and acetylenes. If the color of bromine disappears, addition is presumed to have occurred. Saturated and aromatic compounds are inert to bromine under these conditions. Some oxygen-containing compounds react, however, so it is necessary to establish that the unknown is a hydrocarbon before this test can be trusted. While chlorine and bromine both add readily to a variety of olefins, fluorine or iodine additions are seldom satisfactory. Fluorine is so reactive that it literally "chews up" organic molecules: indiscriminate breakage of carbon-carbon and carbon-hydrogen bonds accompanies attempted addition. Iodine reacts very slowly with most olefins, and the 1,2-diiodides formed decompose readily.

The addition of halogen acids occurs satisfactorily with any HX. The reaction can thus be used to prepare a wide variety of alkyl halides. Reactivity varies in the order HI > HBr > HCl > HF, which is also the order of acid strength. As already noted, addition follows the Markovnikov rule. Thus, the ethyl halide (from ethylene) is the only primary halide accessible by this method. All other olefins will yield secondary or tertiary halides. In a few cases *carbonium-ion rearrangements* may accompany addition:

$$(CH_3)_2\overset{\underset{\displaystyle |}{H}}{C}-CH=CH_2 + HCl \longrightarrow (CH_3)_2\overset{\underset{\displaystyle |}{H}}{C}-\overset{+}{C}H-CH_3 + Cl^-$$

$$(CH_3)_2\overset{\underset{\displaystyle |}{H}}{C}-\overset{+}{C}H-CH_3 \longrightarrow (CH_3)_2\overset{+}{C}-CH_2-CH_3$$

$$(CH_3)_2\overset{+}{C}-CH_2-CH_3 + Cl^- \longrightarrow (CH_3)_2\overset{\underset{\displaystyle |}{Cl}}{C}-CH_2CH_3$$

In this example, hydrogen migrates with its pair of electrons from the adjacent carbon, thereby producing a more stable tertiary carbonium ion. Such rearrangements may occur whenever migration of a hydrogen or an alkyl group from an adjacent carbon atom can convert the first-formed intermediate into a more stable (i.e., more substituted) carbonium ion.

Additions of HOX to olefins produce a class of compounds called halohydrins:

$$CH_2=CH_2 + HOCl \longrightarrow HOCH_2CH_2Cl$$
ethylene chlorohydrin

These additions occur with HOI, HOBr and HOCl. The products are useful synthetic intermediates, as treatment with base removes HX to give a cyclic ether called an *epoxide:*

$$HOCH_2CH_2Cl + NaOH \longrightarrow \overset{\displaystyle O}{\overset{\displaystyle \diagup\,\diagdown}{CH_2-CH_2}} + NaCl + H_2O$$
ethylene oxide

These compounds have rather strained rings (60° bond angles instead of

109°28') and undergo some interesting reactions. We will consider them in the next chapter.

Most other additions involving HX-type addends are either direct or indirect hydrations. Olefins with two alkyl groups on one or both of the doubly-bonded carbons hydrate readily in fairly dilute solutions of strong acids:

$$(CH_3)_2C=CH_2 + H_2O \xrightarrow{\text{1M HNO}_3} (CH_3)_3COH$$

Less-substituted olefins (which would give less-stable carbonium ion intermediates) require higher acid concentration and/or higher temperatures.

Addition of sulfuric acid to an olefin yields an alkyl hydrogen sulfate, which may be readily hydrolyzed to the alcohol:

$$H_2C=CH_2 \xrightarrow{\text{H}_2\text{SO}_4} CH_3CH_2OSO_3H \xrightarrow{\text{H}_2\text{O}} CH_3CH_2OH$$

This sequence of reactions is used industrially to synthesize alcohols from the olefins obtained in the cracking of petroleum hydrocarbons. Another example is

$$CH_3CH_2CH=CH_2 \xrightarrow{\text{H}_2\text{SO}_4} CH_3CH_2\underset{\underset{OSO_3H}{|}}{C}HCH_3 \xrightarrow{\text{H}_2\text{O}} CH_3CH_2\underset{\underset{OH}{|}}{C}HCH_3$$

Note that the addition always follows Markovnikov's rule.

An ingenious method of obtaining alcohols from olefins via a reaction sequence resulting in anti-Markovnikov addition was recently developed by H. C. Brown.† First the olefin is treated with diborane (B_2H_6), and the addition product is then oxidized with alkaline hydrogen peroxide:

$$CH_3CH=CH_2 + B_2H_6 \longrightarrow (CH_3CH_2CH_2)_3B$$

$$(CH_3CH_2CH_2)_3B + 3H_2O_2 \xrightarrow{\text{NaOH}} 3CH_3CH_2CH_2OH + H_3BO_3$$

The detailed mechanism of the reaction is not known, but the reversed orientation probably arises from attack of the electron-deficient BH_3 (formed by dissociation of B_2H_6) on the olefin in such a manner as to yield the more stable carbonium ion:

$$CH_3CH=CH_2 + BH_3 \longrightarrow CH_3\overset{+}{C}H-CH_2\overset{-}{B}H_3$$

The remaining steps involve hydride transfer from boron to carbon, followed by addition of the product to another molecule of olefin, and so on until the trialkylboron results:

$$CH_3\overset{+}{C}H-CH_2\overset{-}{B}H_3 \longrightarrow CH_3CH_2CH_2BH_2$$

$$CH_3CH_2CH_2BH_2 + CH_3CH=CH_2 \longrightarrow (CH_3CH_2CH_2)_2BH \quad \text{etc.}$$

† H. C. Brown. Born 1912 in Great Britain. Now at Purdue University. His scientific interests are wide-ranging and include studies of organoboron compounds, steric effects and aromatic substitution reactions.

Since B_2H_6 is difficult to handle as a pure compound, it is usually generated right in the reaction mixture from the reaction of sodium borohydride with aluminum chloride in "diglyme":

$$CH_3OCH_2CH_2OCH_2CH_2OCH_3.$$

Earlier we saw the preparation of epoxides from olefins via halohydrins. Epoxides can also be prepared by direct oxidation of olefins with peroxyacids (acids in which the OH of the carboxyl group has been replaced by OOH). Some typical procedures are

$$RCH{=}CHR + CF_3\overset{\overset{O}{\|}}{C}OOH \xrightarrow[\text{NaH}_2\text{PO}_4]{\text{CH}_2\text{Cl}_2} RCH\overset{}{\underset{O}{\diagdown\diagup}}CHR$$

and

$$RCH{=}CHR + C_6H_5\overset{\overset{O}{\|}}{C}OOH \xrightarrow{\text{HCCl}_3} RCH\overset{}{\underset{O}{\diagdown\diagup}}CHR$$

In the first example, a buffer (NaH_2PO_4) is needed to prevent attack on the epoxide by the trifluoroacetic acid formed in the reaction.

Such attack may be desired, however, in some applications of the reaction. The use of a performic-formic acid mixture to carry out the epoxidation leads ultimately to a 1,2-diol via the sequence:

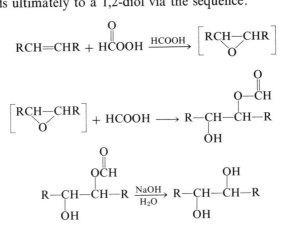

Note that the net result of the reaction is a *trans* addition. Thus, if the reaction had been with cyclopentene, the product would have been *trans*-1,2-cyclopentanediol:

Opening of epoxides generally involves attack on the opposite side of the carbon atom from the epoxide oxygen. Certain direct oxidation procedures may effect *cis*-hydroxylation of a double bond. Osmium tetroxide (OsO_4) gives addition via a cyclic osmate ester, which must be *cis:*

$$\text{RCH=CHR} \xrightarrow{OsO_4} \underset{\underset{\displaystyle OsO_2}{O\diagdown\diagup O}}{\text{RCH}-\text{CHR}} \xrightarrow{H_2O} \underset{\displaystyle OH\quad OH}{\text{RCH}-\text{CHR}}$$

The ring opens with attack on osmium rather than on carbon, so the stereochemistry at both carbon atoms remains the same as that in the osmate ester. This reaction will give hydroxylation even when the double bond bears strongly electron-withdrawing substituents, a circumstance in which the epoxide route usually fails. Osmium tetroxide is toxic and very expensive. It may be conserved by using only a catalytic amount along with hydrogen peroxide to reoxidize the osmic acid obtained in hydrolysis of the osmate ester.

A less exotic method of *cis*-hydroxylation is oxidation by neutral potassium permanganate:

$$\text{3RCH=CHR} + \text{2KMnO}_4 + \text{4H}_2\text{O} \longrightarrow \underset{\displaystyle OH\quad OH}{\text{3RCH}-\text{CHR}} + \text{2MnO}_2 + \text{2KOH}$$

Yields are considerably lower than with osmium tetroxide, because it is difficult to prevent further oxidation of the diol. The reaction has for a long time been used as a qualitative test for unsaturation: decolorization of a dilute potassium permanganate solution by a compound is taken as evidence for unsaturation. The test is not entirely specific, as a positive test will be given by any easily oxidizable organic compounds (aldehydes, for example). Again, as in the case of the bromine test, it is necessary to establish first that the unknown is a hydrocarbon before the test can be deemed reliable.

A particularly interesting oxidation reaction of olefins is that with ozone:

$$\text{RCH=CHR'} + \text{O}_3 \longrightarrow \underset{\displaystyle O\text{------}O}{\overset{\displaystyle O}{\text{R}\overset{\diagup\diagdown}{\text{CH}}\quad\text{CHR'}}}$$

The ozone is prepared by first passing oxygen through an electrical discharge and then bubbling it through a solution of the olefin in an inert solvent. Methylene chloride is often used as solvent, and the reaction mixture is usually kept at 0°C or lower. The addition product, called an *ozonide,* is seldom isolated as such, because it is unstable and liable to explode in the pure state. Decomposition may be effected by simple hydrolysis:

$$\underset{\substack{| \quad\quad\quad |\\ O\!-\!-\!-\!O}}{RCH \quad CHR'} + H_2O \longrightarrow R\overset{\displaystyle O}{\underset{\|}{-}}C-H + R'\overset{\displaystyle O}{\underset{\|}{-}}C-H + H_2O_2$$

Under these conditions, the aldehydes are often further oxidized to carboxylic acids. This oxidation can be avoided by reductive decomposition using hydrogen and a palladium catalyst:

$$\underset{\substack{| \quad\quad\quad |\\ O\!-\!-\!-\!O}}{RCH \quad CHR'} + H_2 \xrightarrow{\text{Pd}} R\overset{\displaystyle O}{\underset{\|}{-}}C-H + R'\overset{\displaystyle O}{\underset{\|}{-}}C-H + H_2O$$

With two alkyl groups on a carbon atom of the double bond, ketones result:

$$R_2C{=}CR_2 \xrightarrow{\text{O}_3} \underset{\substack{| \quad\quad\quad |\\ O\!-\!-\!O}}{R_2C \quad CR_2} \xrightarrow[\text{Pd}]{\text{H}_2} 2R\overset{\displaystyle O}{\underset{\|}{-}}C-R + H_2O$$

Ozonization is very useful in the *degradation* of complex organic molecules, where the aim is to "chop" the molecule into smaller fragments that are easier to identify.

Though the ozonide is the first isolable product, it is formed in a series of steps:

$$R_2C{=}CR_2 + O_3 \longrightarrow \underset{\substack{|\quad\quad|\\ O\!-\!O\!-\!O\\ \quad + \quad -}}{R_2C\!-\!CR_2} \longrightarrow$$

$$R_2C{=}O + \underset{+ \quad\quad -}{R_2C\!-\!O\!-\!O} \longrightarrow \underset{\substack{|\quad\quad|\\ O\!-\!O}}{R_2C \quad CR_2}$$

The first-formed addend breaks up, and the "dipolar ion" adds to the carbonyl group of the ketone.

Olefins, such as isobutylene, that can form relatively stable carbonium ions undergo an acid-catalyzed self addition:

$$(CH_3)_2C{=}CH_2 + H^+ \longrightarrow (CH_3)_3C^+$$

$$(CH_3)_3C^+ + CH_2{=}C(CH_3)_2 \longrightarrow (CH_3)_3C-CH_2\overset{+}{C}(CH_3)_2$$

$$(CH_3)_3CCH_2\overset{+}{C}(CH_3)_2 \longrightarrow H^+ + (CH_3)_3CCH{=}C(CH_3)_2$$

$$+ \; (CH_3)_3CCH_2\underset{\underset{\textstyle CH_3}{|}}{C}{=}CH_2$$

The mixture of olefins formed is known by the trivial name of *diisobutylene.*

In principle, the carbonium ion formed in the addition could add to more isobutylene instead of losing a proton. Some products containing three or more isobutylene units are formed, but apparently the ion is so hindered by its high degree of chain branching that further addition is very slow.

A related reaction is the alkylation of isobutane by isobutylene in the presence of 85–100% sulfuric acid or liquid hydrogen fluoride. The overall reaction is:

$$(CH_3)_3CH + CH_2\!\!=\!\!C(CH_3)_2 \xrightarrow{\text{85-100\% H}_2\text{SO}_4} (CH_3)_3CCH_2CH(CH_3)_2$$

The reaction is initiated in the same manner as the self-addition of isobutylene: a carbonium ion is formed and then adds to another molecule of isobutylene to give a new carbonium ion. In the presence of isobutane this carbonium ion abstracts the tertiary hydrogen atom with its pair of electrons:

$$(CH_3)_3CCH_2\overset{+}{C}[CH_3]_2 + (CH_3)_3CH \longrightarrow (CH_3)_3CCH_2\overset{\overset{\displaystyle H}{|}}{C}(CH_3)_2 + (CH_3)_3C^+$$

The *t*-butyl carbonium ion can now initiate another reaction of the same kind by adding to a molecule of isobutylene. The reaction is thus an example of *chain reaction*, for one of the products serves to initiate still further reaction. Alkylations such as this are very useful in preparing the branched-chain hydrocarbons used in modern high-octane gasoline.

So far we have covered many of the important ionic addition reactions of olefins. Additions to olefins possessing unsaturated, strongly electron-withdrawing substituents on the double bond have been omitted, as these will be covered elsewhere in this series†. Briefly, such reactions are distinguished from those that have been treated here, because they are initiated by attack with a *nucleophilic* (electron-rich) reagent and often involve basic, rather than acidic, catalysts. One example, among many, is the addition of an amine to acrylonitrile:

$$R_2NH + CH_2\!\!=\!\!CHCN \longrightarrow R_2NCH_2CH_2CN$$

A number of other reactions worth mentioning do not fit into the category of ionic addition reactions. The most important of these is the addition of hydrogen. This is a heterogeneous reaction, occurring on the surface of a metal catalyst. Both the olefin and the hydrogen are adsorbed on the surface of the catalyst. The exact mechanisms by which the catalyst brings them together and enhances their reactivity are not well understood. The reaction is simply:

$$RCH\!\!=\!\!CHR + H_2 \xrightarrow[\text{catalyst}]{\text{metal}} RCH_2CH_2R$$

† C. D. Gutsche, *op. cit.*

The metals most often used are platinum, palladium and nickel. Because reaction occurs at the surface of the catalyst, large surface area is important. Very finely divided platinum and palladium are obtained by reduction of their salts with hydrogen. A spongy form of nickel called Raney nickel, which has large surface area, is produced by dissolving the aluminum from an aluminum-nickel alloy with sodium hydroxide. Hydrogenation is very widely applicable, though it may be difficult with olefins which have four alkyl groups attached to the double bond. In such compounds, adsorption on the catalyst is apparently hindered.

A reaction which has excited considerable recent interest is the addition of an unstable intermediate known as a *carbene* to a double bond. Carbenes may be generated in various ways; one of the most common is by attack of a base on a *haloform* (a compound of the type HCX_3, where X is a halogen). An example is:

$$HCCl_3 + OH^- \rightleftharpoons {}^-:CCl_3 + H_2O$$

$$^-:CCl_3 \rightleftharpoons :CCl_2 + Cl^-$$

A cyclopropane is the usual product of carbene addition. Note that the carbene is electron-deficient, having only six electrons in the outer shell of the carbon atom, but it possesses no charge.

The addition reactions of acetylenes are analogous to those of olefins. Halogens add in two stages, giving first an olefin and then a saturated product:

$$RC{\equiv}CH + X_2 \longrightarrow \underset{\underset{X}{|}}{R}C{=}\underset{\underset{X}{|}}{C}H$$

$$\underset{\underset{X}{|}}{R}C{=}\underset{\underset{X}{|}}{C}H + X_2 \longrightarrow R{-}\underset{\underset{X}{\overset{\overset{X}{|}}{|}}}{C}{-}\underset{\underset{X}{\overset{\overset{X}{|}}{|}}}{C}{-}H$$

Generally it is difficult to stop these additions at the olefin stage, for acetylenes tend to be less reactive than olefins, and conditions which are adequate for the first stage promote the second as well. Additions of HX have been described in Sec. 2.6.

An especially interesting addition reaction of acetylenes is that which occurs with water. It is catalyzed by mercuric salts and yields initially an enol (an unsaturated alcohol with the hydroxyl group attached directly to the double bond). Enols are unstable, and the final product is a carbonyl compound:

$$HC\equiv CH + H_2O \xrightarrow[HgSO_4]{H_2SO_4} [H_2C=CHOH]$$

$$[H_2C=CHOH] \longrightarrow CH_3\overset{\overset{\displaystyle O}{\|}}{C}H$$
$$\text{acetaldehyde}$$

$$RC\equiv CH + H_2O \xrightarrow[HgSO_4]{H_2SO_4} \left[R\overset{\overset{\displaystyle OH}{|}}{C}=CH_2 \right]$$

$$\left[R\overset{\overset{\displaystyle OH}{|}}{C}=CH_2 \right] \longrightarrow R\overset{\overset{\displaystyle O}{\|}}{C}CH_3$$

Note again that Markovnikov's rule is followed with the monoalkyl acetylene.

Reduction of acetylenes also occurs in stages:

$$RC\equiv CR + H_2 \longrightarrow RCH=CHR$$

$$RCH=CHR + H_2 \longrightarrow RCH_2CH_2R$$

With platinum and hydrogen, reduction proceeds to the saturated hydrocarbon. With palladium or Raney nickel and hydrogen, the addition may be stopped at the olefin stage under appropriate conditions. The product in these cases is that of *cis* addition:

$$RC\equiv CR + H_2 \xrightarrow{\text{Raney Ni}} \overset{R}{\underset{H}{\diagdown}}C=C\overset{R}{\underset{H}{\diagup}}$$

Unlike simple olefins, acetylenes undergo reduction by sodium in liquid ammonia. Here the product is the *trans* olefin:

$$RC\equiv CR + 2Na + 2NH_3 \longrightarrow \overset{H}{\underset{R}{\diagdown}}C=C\overset{R}{\underset{H}{\diagup}} + 2NaNH_2$$

No precautions are necessary to prevent further reduction of the olefin, so this is the best method for the preparation of olefins from acetylenes unless a *cis* olefin is wanted.

CHAPTER 2 REVIEW QUESTIONS

1. Explain why addition of bromine to double bonds is stereospecific *trans*.

2. Predict the orientation of addition in the following reactions:

    (a) $CH_3OCH{=}CH_2 + HBr$ (b) $(CH_3)_2C{=}CHCH_3 + HOCl$
    (c) $CH_3CH{=}CH_2 + ICl$

3. Why does HBr sometimes add to simple olefins in a manner contrary to Markovnikov's rule?

4. Why are acetylenes generally less reactive than olefins toward addition reactions?

5. How could both 1-butanol and 2-butanol be prepared from 1-butene?

6. How could both the *cis* and *trans* isomers of 1,2-cyclopentanediol be prepared from cyclopentene?

3

Nucleophilic Substitution

3.1 DEFINITIONS

A substitution reaction is just what the name implies; i.e., a process in which one atom or group of atoms in a molecule is replaced by another. *Nucleophilic* (literally, *nucleus-loving*) substitutions are those in which the incoming group furnishes both electrons of the new covalent bond, and the departing group takes with it the electron pair of the breaking bond. Schematically, the picture is

$$Y: + R:X \longrightarrow Y:R + :X$$

We have pictured both reactants as electrically neutral in this general equation. Other charge types may also undergo the reaction: the only absolute limitation is the usual one for all chemical reactions, that the total charge on the right be equal to that on the left side of the balanced equation. A few specific examples of nucleophilic substitutions are:

$$RCl + H_2O \longrightarrow ROH + HCl$$

$$R'Br + RO^- \longrightarrow R'OR + Br^-$$

$$HO^- + CH_3\overset{+}{N}(CH_3)_3 \longrightarrow CH_3OH + N(CH_3)_3$$

$$(CH_3)_3N + CH_3I \longrightarrow (CH_3)_3\overset{+}{N}CH_3 + I^-$$

Many more examples will be cited later, but these reactions suffice to illustrate the wide applicability of nucleophilic substitutions. Indeed, there is probably no other type of organic reaction that has been more thoroughly investigated mechanistically, or more widely used synthetically.

Before examining the mechanisms of these reactions, we will point out a few generalizations. The *nucleophilic reagent* (Y in the general equation) almost always becomes attached to the *substrate* (RX) at the carbon atom to which the *leaving group* (X) was attached. When it becomes attached to a different carbon atom, a *rearrangement* is said to have occurred. Normally, we wish to perform a reaction under conditions that minimize the chances of rearrangement so that we can be sure of the structure of the product. Examples of reactions without and with rearrangement are, respectively:

$$CH_3CH_2CH_2Br + OH^- \longrightarrow CH_3CH_2CH_2OH + Br^-$$

$$CH_3CH_2CH_2NH_2 + HNO_2 \longrightarrow CH_3\underset{\underset{\displaystyle OH}{|}}{C}HCH_3 + N_2 + H_2O$$

In the second equation, the OH is attached to the carbon atom next to the one that bore the NH_2 in the reactant. Ways of suppressing or promoting rearrangement will be discussed after the mechanisms have been presented.

Many of the generalizations about substitution reactions are to a considerable extent independent of the nature of the functional groups involved. We may thus make the same deductions about, say, the effect of the structure of the alkyl group on reactivity in reactions as diverse as ether synthesis and the hydrolysis of quaternary ammonium salts.

Finally, nucleophilic substitutions, like most organic reactions, are usually not simple processes that yield 100% of the amount of product expected from the amounts of reactants used. One *side reaction* that often accompanies substitution is elimination to form an olefin. Elimination reactions will be discussed separately in Chap. 4, and means of predicting and regulating their contribution to the total (substitution + elimination) reaction will be covered in Chap. 5. In the meantime, equations showing a single organic product are not meant to imply the complete absence of side reactions.

3.2 THE S_N2 MECHANISM

Before any additional useful generalizations can be made, we must discuss the mechanisms of substitution reactions. There are two important mechanisms; which of these applies in a given case depends upon the structure of the reactant and the reaction conditions. For the present, we will give typical examples of each, and discuss later which mechanisms apply in which sets of circumstances.

When methyl bromide is dissolved in aqueous sodium hydroxide solution, it slowly hydrolyzes to methyl alcohol:

$$CH_3Br + OH^- \longrightarrow CH_3OH + Br^-$$

The rate of the reaction can be determined by following the rate of either disappearance of base or appearance of bromide ion. This rate is found to be proportional to the concentrations of both methyl bromide and hydroxide ion:

$$\text{rate} = k_2[CH_3Br][OH^-]$$

The mechanism by which this reaction occurs was named the *S_N2 mecha-*

nism by C. K. Ingold.† The symbols stand for substitution, nucleophilic, bimolecular. The word *bimolecular* means that two molecules, the substrate and the nucleophile, are involved in the rate-determining step of the reaction.

The path by which the reaction occurs is through attack of hydroxide ion on the side of the carbon atom *opposite* that to which the bromine is attached. During the same time that a bond is forming between the carbon atom and the hydroxide ion, the carbon-bromine bond is weakening. When the carbon-oxygen bond is completely formed, the carbon-bromine bond is completely broken. The process can be visualized as

The entity in brackets is the transition state, the highest energy point in the reaction. The hydroxide ion displaces the bromide ion, the formation of the carbon-oxygen bond providing the energy necessary to break the carbon-bromine bond. The latter process without the former would be much less favored, as more energy (in the form of heat) would be needed to replace that resulting from bond formation. The other conceivable stepwise process, formation of the carbon-oxygen bond first, is impossible because carbon cannot possess more than four covalent bonds. The S$_N$2 reaction is thus a *concerted* process which occurs in one step without any intermediates.

3.3 THE S$_N$1 MECHANISM

Under some circumstances, prior carbon-halogen bond cleavage may not be as unfavorable as it is in the example given above. The circumstances might be expected to include a highly branched substrate (making the central carbon atom difficult to approach), a solvent that promotes ionization, and the absence of a good nucleophile. The appropriate combination of factors seems to be present in the hydrolysis of *t*-butyl chloride, as this reaction occurs in aqueous solution without the need for added base:

$$(CH_3)_3CCl + H_2O \longrightarrow (CH_3)_3COH + HCl$$

The rate of the reaction, measurable by following the appearance of either

---

† C. K. Ingold. Born 1893. English. Professor of Chemistry at University College, London (now retired). Outstanding and extensive contributions to our knowledge of reaction mechanisms, especially of nucleophilic substitution, electrophilic substitution, and elimination reactions.

the acid or the chloride ion, depends only on the concentration of t-butyl chloride:

$$\text{rate} = k_1[(CH_3)_3CCl]$$

Added hydroxide ion (at least in small concentrations) has no effect on the rate. The mechanism of this reaction is called S_N1 (substitution, nucleophilic, unimolecular). Only the t-butyl chloride molecule, without any added nucleophile, is involved in the rate-determining step.

The path of this reaction has two distinct steps, the first of which is the slower in nearly all circumstances:

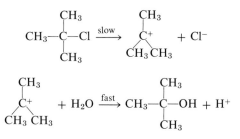

The intermediate, formed in the first step and destroyed in the second, is a *carbonium ion*. As noted in Chap. 1, it has only six electrons in the outer shell of the central carbon; consequently, it reacts readily with any substance possessing an unshared electron pair (in this case, a water molecule).

Usually, the carbonium-ion intermediate in an S_N1 reaction is so unstable and reactive that it cannot be observed directly in any way. While the mechanism pictured above explains the facts most satisfactorily, it is not the only possibility. We might argue, for example, that the reaction was really an S_N2 displacement with water acting as the nucleophile. It is difficult to understand why water should function in this fashion when the stronger nucleophile, hydroxide ion, has no effect on the reaction rate (see above). Such facts make it unlikely that the S_N2 mechanism is involved in this reaction, but do not exclude it entirely. What is clearly needed is some positive evidence that the reaction does have an *intermediate*. This type of evidence would exclude the S_N2 mechanism, which occurs in a single stage without any intermediates.

Evidence for the carbonium-ion intermediate in S_N1 reactions comes from various experiments. One of the most striking pieces of evidence is observable only in reactions with unusually stable carbonium ions as intermediates. For reasons that we will discuss later (Chap. 6), aryl groups attached to the carbon atom bearing the positive charge increase the stability of the carbonium ion. Thus, benzhydryl bromide (a short name for diphenylcarbinyl bromide, $(C_6H_5)_2CHBr$) readily yields a stable carbonium ion. When benzhydryl bromide is hydrolyzed in an acetone-water mixture, the rate "constant" for the S_N1 reaction decreases as the reaction proceeds. If excess bromide ion (for example, sodium bromide) is added, the reaction is slower from the beginning.

This set of circumstances is consistent only with a reaction having an intermediate which can react either with water to give the final product or with bromide ion to regenerate starting material:

$$RBr \rightleftharpoons R^+ + Br^-$$
$$R^+ + H_2O \longrightarrow ROH + H^+$$

Addition of excess bromide ion causes more of the carbonium ions to go back to RBr, and thus reduces the rate of formation of ROH. The same effect results from the bromide ion produced in the reaction; as its concentration increases, the proportion of carbonium ions returning to RBr increases. This *mass-law effect* (the term comes from the law of mass action) is not observed in all S_N1 reactions. Simple alkyl halides, such as *t*-butyl chloride and bromide, apparently give very unstable carbonium ions that are "snapped up" by reaction with solvent as soon as they are formed; they have little chance of existing long enough to encounter halide ions, which are far less numerous than solvent molecules.

More recent evidence, mainly from the work of Winstein,† shows that some S_N1 reactions have *ion pairs* as intermediates. In these cases the covalent carbon-halogen bond is broken, but the two fragments remain closely associated as R^+X^-. In some instances the ion pairs seem to react directly with solvent to give the final products; in others, they seem to dissociate to free ions first. Ion pairs are most often encountered in acetic acid and similar solvents that are sufficiently polar for the promotion of ionization, but not very efficient for solvating free ions. A detailed discussion of ion pairs would rapidly become too complex for an elementary text, so the subject is only mentioned in passing. An important practical consequence of ion-pair mechanisms is that carbonium ions prone to rearrangement (see later discussion, and also Chap. 6) may rearrange at the ion-pair stage and then return to covalent reactant. The reactant may thus be converted from RX to some isomeric compound R'X faster than it undergoes the S_N1 reaction.

3.4 STEREOCHEMISTRY OF SUBSTITUTION

Additional support for the two substitution mechanisms is found in the stereochemistry of their products. In presenting the S_N2 mechanism,

† S. Winstein. Born 1912 in Canada. Now at University of California at Los Angeles. Mechanisms of solvolysis reactions, especially neighboring group effects and ion-pair phenomena.

we used an example in which hydroxide ion displaces bromide ion from methyl bromide. The hydroxide ion was shown attacking the side of the carbon atom opposite to that at which the bromide is attached. Actually, it is impossible to distinguish this process from one in which the hydroxide ion comes in on the *same* side as the bromine atom, for

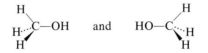

are just different ways of writing the same molecule. However, if an *optically-active* alkyl halide is used, *retention* (incoming group on the same side as the departing group) can be distinguished from *inversion* (incoming group on the opposite side from the departing group).

This argument can be illustrated with 2-butyl bromide. If the reaction with hydroxide ion gave retention, the result would be

$$\underset{CH_3}{\overset{C_2H_5}{H\cdots C-Br}} + OH^- \longrightarrow \underset{CH_3}{\overset{C_2H_5}{H\cdots C-OH}}$$

while if it gave inversion, the result would be

$$\underset{CH_3}{\overset{C_2H_5}{H\cdots C-Br}} + OH^- \longrightarrow HO-\underset{CH_3}{\overset{C_2H_5}{C\cdots H}}$$

Now the two products are no longer identical, but are *mirror images* or *enantiomers* of each other. One of these products will rotate polarized light to the left, and the other will rotate it to the right. Such experiments have shown that all S_N2 reactions proceed with *inversion* of configuration (enough different cases have been studied to make it virtually certain that inversion is the rule even where it has not been formally established).

A disadvantage of the approach described above is that we need to *relate* the configurations of the alkyl halide and the alcohol, for an alcohol with the same sign of rotation as the alkyl halide may or may not have the same configuration. Configurations of two compounds can, in principle, be related simply by converting one to the other, using either reactions that do not break any bonds to the asymmetric carbon atom, or else reactions of known stereochemistry. In practice this may be very tedious or difficult.

An ingenious way to avoid this problem was devised by Ingold. Suppose we allow an optically-active alkyl iodide to react with *radioactive* iodide ion. Let $(+)$-RI represent one enantiomer, $(-)$-RI the other, and I^{*-} the radioactive iodide. The S_N2 reaction then would be

$$(+)\text{-RI} + I^{*-} \longrightarrow (-)\text{-RI*} + I^-$$

Each attack of iodide ion gives an RI of opposite configuration. Since the rotation due to this new molecule exactly cancels that due to an unreacted molecule, the alkyl iodide will lose its optical activity *twice* as fast as it picks up radioactivity. If the reaction occurs with retention, no change in optical activity will accompany the gain in radioactivity. The actual results demonstrate that inversion occurs. Later we will see that a different stereochemical result is predicted for the S_N1 reaction, so that this method can be used to distinguish S_N1 from S_N2.

In an S_N1 reaction, the product is formed from a carbonium-ion intermediate, and the stereochemistry of the product therefore depends upon the stereochemistry of the intermediate. Theory and experimental evidence both suggest that carbonium ions are *planar*. The carbon atom possessing the charge is sp^2 hybridized, so that the groups attached to it are in a plane and the bond angles between them are $120°$:

The ion possesses a plane of symmetry (the plane of the paper in our illustration). Attack by a solvent molecule (or other nucleophilic reagent) should occur with equal probability on either side of the plane. Regardless of whether the starting material was ($+$) or ($-$), the product should be a 50:50 mixture of ($+$) and ($-$) isomers, i.e., *racemic*.

In fact, there is considerable racemization in S_N1 reactions, but there is also usually some product of inverted configuration. In our reasoning detailed above, we have neglected the fact that the carbonium ion is not alone in the solvent. Unless the ion has an unusually long life, it will still be rather close to the *leaving group* that was present in the starting material. The leaving group will partially shield the front side of the carbonium ion, and attack by solvent will be easier at the back side. More product of inverted than of retained configuration results, and hence some inversion accompanies racemization.

A similar way of viewing the S_N1 reaction emphasizes more explicitly the role of solvation (the association of solvent molecules with a molecule or ion). In the following, SOH represents a solvent molecule:

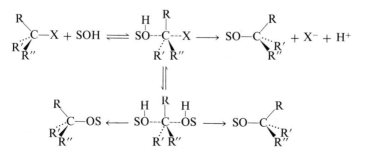

The first intermediate formed is asymmetrically solvated (by SOH on one side and X on the other) and the product of its collapse to a stable molecule will be either starting material or *inverted* solvolysis product. If the first intermediate survives long enough, it can lose the leaving group altogether and become the symmetrically-solvated second intermediate. This second intermediate collapses to give equal amounts of inverted and retained product; i.e., a racemic mixture. The picture presented above predicts that the more stable the carbonium ion is, the more racemization will result, for it will have more chance to become symmetrically solvated. The experimental results confirm this prediction.

We can now return to a subject mentioned while discussing the stereochemistry of S_N2 reactions: that is, the result to be expected in an S_N1 exchange of alkyl iodides with iodide ion. The sequence of reactions would be

$$(+)\text{-RI} \longrightarrow R^+ \xrightarrow{\quad I^{*-} \quad} \begin{array}{l} (+)\text{-RI}^* \\ (-)\text{-RI}^* \end{array}$$
$$[\text{symmetrical}]$$

It is unnecessary to show explicitly the solvation of the carbonium ion, as it would always be "solvated" by two iodide ions and thus be symmetrical (I^- and I^{*-} do not differ sufficiently to confer detectable asymmetry). Each R^+ formed has a 50:50 chance of giving $(+)$ or $(-)$ product. On the average, then, exchange of two molecules of RI would give one $(+)$-RI* and one $(-)$-RI*; exchange of four would give two of each; and so on. The conclusion we reach is that loss of optical activity and uptake of radioactive iodine should occur at the *same* rate in an S_N1 reaction, as compared to the 2:1 ratio predicted (and observed) for the S_N2 reaction.

3.5 EFFECTS OF STRUCTURE AND SOLVENT ON REACTIVITY

So far we have presented much information about S_N1 and S_N2 reactions, but little about the circumstances that favor one reaction over another. How we can predict which mechanism will apply in a given reaction of a particular reactant will be discussed below. In general, we must consider the nature of the alkyl group, the nature of the leaving group, and the nature of the reaction conditions, including added nucleophile, if any.

The causes behind the effects of structure on reactivity are somewhat simpler to deduce for S_N1 reactions, so they will be considered first. The slow step in an S_N1 reaction is formation of the carbonium ion. Thus, the transition state for the reaction will have a structure somewhere between that of the reactant and that of the carbonium ion. (In Chap. 1, we saw that an unstable intermediate and the transition state leading to it are usually similar in structure.)

If the transition state resembles the carbonium ion, it should be stabilized by the same factors that stabilize a carbonium ion. Electron-repelling alkyl groups help the carbonium ion to bear the positive charge, so carbonium ion stability runs: tertiary > secondary > primary. Similarly, in S_N1 reactions, the sequence of reactivity for a typical set of reactants is

$$(CH_3)_3CX > (CH_3)_2CHX > CH_3CH_2X > CH_3X$$

This sequence is so pronounced that it is difficult to avoid S_N1 reactions with tertiary halides and difficult to make them occur at all with primary halides.

Another deduction we can make is that anything which prevents attainment of the planar structure favored by the carbonium ion hinders reaction. Thus, *bridged compounds* such as

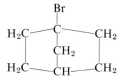

are very unreactive in S_N1 reactions, because of the distortions in normal bond angles that would be required for coplanarity of the carbon which bears the bromine and the three methylene groups. Similarly, cyclopropyl halides are very unreactive, because the bonds cannot spread out to the 120° angle of the groups attached to a symmetrical carbonium ion. Broadly, this effect applies to cyclic compounds in general, but the trend is not entirely regular with ring size because of special circumstances too complex to go into here.

Conversely, factors favoring a planar carbonium ion increase reactivity. If the R's in R_3CX are very large and bulky (R = t-butyl, for example), they will have more room in the carbonium ion (where R—C—R bond angles are 120°) than in the reactant (where R—C—R bond angles are 109°28′). Since strain is released in the reaction, large alkyl groups confer a larger-than-expected rate to an S_N1 reaction. This contribution to reactivity has been named *I-strain* (*I* for *internal*) by H. C. Brown.

The dependence of structure on reactivity for S_N2 reactions is almost exactly opposite that for S_N1 reactions. A typical sequence for the former is

$$CH_3X > CH_3CH_2X > (CH_3)_2CHX > (CH_3)_3CX$$

Here chain branching slows the reaction, probably because of a steric effect. Since the nucleophilic reagent must approach the back of the carbon bearing the leaving group X, branching and/or bulky groups will get in the way. Thus, bridged compounds of the type shown above are completely inert. Another possible factor is the electron-repelling inductive effect of alkyl groups, which would make the carbon atom more electron-rich and less attractive to a nucleophilic reagent. At present, most chemists assign a minor role to this factor.

The overall consequence of the reactivity sequence for S_N1 and S_N2 reactions is that primary halides almost always react by the S_N2 mechanism, and tertiary halides almost always react by the S_N1 mechanism. Secondary halides may react by either, depending upon the reaction conditions.

The S_N1 reaction is favored by highly ionizing solvents. Water is the most effective solvent for promoting ionization, but many organic compounds (alkyl halides, in particular) are very slightly soluble in it. Pure formic acid is an effective ionizing solvent, followed at some distance by glacial (100%) acetic acid. Mixed solvents, such as methanol-water, ethanol-water and acetone-water are more effective as their proportion of water is increased. Pure methanol is moderately good, but other pure alcohols are relatively poor. A representative order is

$$CH_3OH > CH_3CH_2OH > (CH_3)_2CHOH > (CH_3)_3COH$$

Non-hydroxylic solvents are almost all poor at promoting ionization.

In the presence of an added strong nucleophile, the S_N2 reaction is favored even in ionizing solvents such as water. In general, anions are more effective as nucleophiles than neutral molecules. Hydroxide ion and ethoxide ion are better than water and ethanol, respectively. Among the anions, *polarizability* seems to be an important factor. A highly polarizable ion will have outer shell electrons that are rather loosely held, so that the electron cloud is easily deformed. Thus, the halide ions are in the order $I^- > Br^- > Cl^- > F^-$, the larger and more polarizable ones being favored. Similarly SH^- is better than OH^-, and sulfur-containing ions (such as $SO_3^=$ and $S_2O_3^=$) are usually good nucleophiles. A few ions such as CN^- and N_3^- seem to owe their effectiveness to their small size, which enables them to slip in to the site of reaction more easily.

Solvation of anions also seems to affect their reactivity. For example, the trend of nucleophilic reactivities for halide ions appears to be $Cl^- > Br^- > I^-$ in dimethylformamide ($HCON(CH_3)_2$). This fact suggests that the opposite order is observed in hydroxylic solvents because hydrogen bonding to solvent is more effective in reducing the reactivity of the smaller anions. Doubt is thus cast on the role of polarizability, but not enough information is available to say that it is generally unimportant.

The effect of solvent on S_N2 reactions depends on the charges of the reactants. The most common case is reaction of an anion with a neutral molecule, in which the charge originally concentrated on the anion becomes dispersed between it and the leaving group in the transition state:

$$Y^- + RX \longrightarrow [(\delta_-)Y\text{---}R\text{---}X(\delta_-)] \longrightarrow YR + X^-$$

(Here the δ_- signifies a partial negative charge.) A good ionizing solvent slows down such a reaction, for it stabilizes the reactant more effectively than it stabilizes the transition state. Ethanol, or even a less polar solvent such as acetone, is to be preferred to water. In practice, we must choose a solvent that will dissolve both reactants. Though a very non-polar solvent such as hexane might be desirable in principle, it would not dissolve the salts of the anionic nucleophiles.

The arguments in the last paragraph do not apply to reactions of different charge types. Generally, a reaction in which charge is dispersed or destroyed in the transition state will be slowed by polar solvents, and one in which charge is produced will be favored by polar solvents. A few examples will suffice to illustrate this reasoning:

$$X^- + (CH_3)_3S^+ \longrightarrow CH_3X + (CH_3)_2S \qquad \text{(charge destroyed)}$$
slowed by polar solvent

$$CH_3Br + (CH_3)_3N \longrightarrow (CH_3)_4N^+ + Br^- \qquad \text{(charge produced)}$$
accelerated by polar solvent

Similar reasoning applies to S_N1 reactions, where charged substrates react more slowly in polar solvents:

$$RS(CH_3)_2^+ \longrightarrow \overset{\delta+}{R}\text{---}\overset{\delta+}{S}(CH_3)_2 \qquad \text{(charge dispersed)}$$
slowed by polar solvent

The effect of the leaving group in both S_N1 and S_N2 reactions is relatively simple. The more easily the bond to the leaving group is broken, the more reactive the substance will be. Reactivity of alkyl halides runs: $RI > RBr > RCl > RF$; this is the accepted order of carbon-halogen bond strengths. Since the leaving group acquires the pair of electrons that originally bound it to carbon, anything that makes it more electron-withdrawing aids reaction. For example, alcohols, ethers and amines are usually inert to either S_N1 or S_N2 reactions. Imparting a positive charge by protonation or alkylation produces

$$ROH_2^+, R_2OH^+ \text{ and } RN(CH_3)_3^+$$

all of which can now undergo displacement reactions.

3.6 REARRANGEMENTS

So far, we have assumed that nucleophilic substitution leaves the alkyl group structurally unchanged; i.e., that the entering group becomes attached to the same carbon as the leaving group. In most cases this assumption is justified, but, especially in some S_N1 reactions, it is possible that *rearrangements* may occur. Hard-and-fast rules cannot be formulated, although rearrangements are most likely to occur when normal reaction would produce a very unstable carbonium ion. When this carbonium ion can be converted to a more stable one by migration of an atom or group from an adjacent carbon (a *1,2 shift*), the chance of rearrangement is greatest. For example, neopentyl derivatives are reluctant to undergo S_N2 reactions because of the large *t*-butyl group attached to the α-carbon, and S_N1 reactions would produce a primary carbonium ion. The path actually taken is migration of a methyl group, which produces a tertiary carbonium ion:

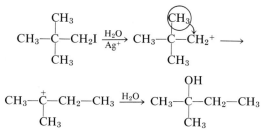

Note that the methyl group migrates *with* its pair of electrons, and thus, in turn, leaves the β-carbon electron deficient. The more stable tertiary carbonium ion then reacts with water. Most efforts to perform substitution reactions on neopentyl derivatives result in rearrangement.

Migration of hydrogen may also occur:

$$(CH_3)_2\overset{H}{\underset{OSO_2C_7H_7}{C-CHCH_3}} \xrightarrow{\text{HCOOH}} (CH_3)_2\overset{\textcircled{H}}{C-\overset{+}{C}HCH_3} \longrightarrow$$

$$(CH_3)_2\overset{+}{C}-\overset{H}{C}HCH_3 \xrightarrow{\text{HCOOH}} (CH_3)_2\overset{\overset{O}{\parallel}}{\underset{}{C}}{-CH_2CH_3}$$

Rearrangements do not normally occur except when a more stable carbonium ion can be produced, and often do not occur even then. Primary reactants, except for special cases where the S_N2 reaction is highly hindered, usually give unrearranged products even under conditions designed to promote S_N1 reaction. Probably a "free" primary carbonium ion is never produced in these cases, and the reaction is essentially an S_N2 displacement by a solvent molecule. When we can be reasonably sure a free carbonium ion is involved, as in decomposition of a diazonium salt from an amine, rearrangement is observed:

$$CH_3CH_2CH_2NH_2 \xrightarrow{\text{HNO}_2} CH_3CH_2CH_2N_2^+ \longrightarrow$$

$$CH_3CH_2CH_2^+ \xrightarrow{H_2O} CH_3CH_2CH_2OH$$

$$\downarrow$$

$$CH_3\overset{+}{C}HCH_3 \xrightarrow{H_2O} CH_3\overset{OH}{\underset{}{C}}HCH_3$$

More isopropyl than *n*-propyl alcohol is obtained. The diazonium ion apparently loses nitrogen so readily that it does not need any help from a solvent molecule.

One must also expect possible rearrangements in reactions performed under reversible conditions; i.e., when the product is not stable as formed but repeatedly goes back to carbonium ion. Thus, rearrangement of one secondary structure to form another does not usually occur, but treatment of 2-pentanol with HBr or PBr$_3$ may give some 3-pentyl as well as 2-pentyl bromide if reaction conditions are too strenuous:

$$CH_3CH_2CH_2\underset{\underset{OH}{|}}{C}HCH_3 \xrightarrow{PBr_3} CH_3CH_2CH_2\underset{\underset{Br}{|}}{C}HCH_3 + CH_3CH_2\underset{\underset{Br}{|}}{C}HCH_2CH_3$$

Whether such problems do or do not arise is so dependent on specific reaction conditions that reliable prediction is difficult. The best policy is to use S$_N$2 reactions wherever possible. If no S$_N$2 reaction will work, use the mildest possible conditions for S$_N$1 reactions.

Certain types of unsaturated halides can undergo rearrangement rather readily. These *allylic rearrangements* will be discussed in Chap. 6, where effects of unsaturated and aromatic substituents on reactivity will be considered.

3.7 SYNTHETIC APPLICATIONS

Very many common synthetic procedures involve the replacement of one group by another. There is considerable advantage in considering these together rather than in separate discussions of the various organic functional groups. In this way, the underlying similarities in effects of structure on reactivity can be emphasized, and the reasons for choosing a particular set of reaction conditions better understood.

The synthesis, and many of the reactions, of alcohols furnish numerous examples. A common way of preparing alcohols is by the hydrolysis of alkyl halides. The conditions chosen depend on the structure of the halide. Primary halides, which react by the S$_N$2 mechanism, react much more readily in basic than in acid or neutral solution because hydroxide ion is a much better nucleophile than water. On the contrary, tertiary halides give very poor yields of alcohol in basic solution; most of the product is olefin, formed in an elimination reaction (see Chap. 5). Respectable yields of tertiary alcohol may in many cases be obtained by hydrolysis in water with no added reagents.

The reverse of the first reaction, conversion of alcohols to alkyl halides, is also important. Commercial preparation of alkyl halides usually involves direct halogenation of hydrocarbons. Mixtures of products containing different position isomers (such as *n*-propyl chloride and isopropyl chloride, from propane) and different numbers of halogen atoms per molecule (such as methyl chloride, methylene chloride, etc., from methane) are usually formed. When a single pure alkyl halide is desired, the corresponding alcohol is often the starting material.

The simplest procedure is reaction of the concentrated halogen acid with the alcohol:

$$(CH_3)_3COH + HCl \longrightarrow (CH_3)_3CCl + H_2O$$

In the example, shaking *t*-butyl alcohol with concentrated hydrochloric acid suffices. However, primary and secondary halides do not react so well. The reaction is facilitated by addition of zinc chloride as a catalyst. A mixture of zinc chloride and hydrochloric acid is the reagent for the *Lucas*† *test:* tertiary alcohols react immediately, secondary alcohols after a few minutes, and primary alcohols very slowly. The appearance of a separate layer of alkyl chloride (immiscible with the aqueous reagent) signals a positive test. Hydrobromic and hydriodic acids also convert alcohols to alkyl halides.

Other common preparations of alkyl halides use more complex reagents. Thionyl chloride converts alcohols to alkyl chlorides:

$$ROH + SOCl_2 \longrightarrow RCl + SO_2 + HCl$$

Initial formation of an ester (not usually isolated) is followed by reaction with chloride ion:

$$ROH + SOCl_2 \longrightarrow ROSOCl + HCl$$

$$Cl^- + ROSOCl \longrightarrow RCl + SO_2 + Cl^-$$

This reaction is of particular interest in that the stereochemical result can vary from almost complete retention to almost complete inversion. In inert solvents there is little or no free chloride ion, and the chloride comes directly from the ester in an intramolecular reaction:

$$R\text{—}Cl + SO_2$$

This is called the $S_N i$ *mechanism* (substitution, nucleophilic, internal). The attack is necessarily on the front side of the carbon. In the presence of an added base such as pyridine (C_5H_5N), the HCl produced in the first step is converted to a salt ($C_5H_5NH^+Cl^-$), and the resulting chloride ion performs an $S_N 2$ displacement with, of course, inversion.

Certain halides of phosphorus also convert alcohols to halides. These

† H. J. Lucas, 1885–1963. American. Professor of Chemistry at California Institute of Technology. A pioneer in the study of organic reaction mechanisms and the effect of structure on reactivity.

reactions probably proceed via phosphite or phosphate ester intermediates. Two examples are:

$$3ROH + PBr_3 \longrightarrow 3RBr + H_3PO_3$$

$$ROH + PCl_5 \longrightarrow RCl + POCl_3 + HCl$$

Often, alcohols are converted to alkyl halides (or to numerous other substances) by first preparing and isolating an ester which is reactive in displacement reactions. Carboxylic esters are not reactive, but sulfonate esters are. A very common one is the *p*-toluenesulfonate, popularly called *tosylate* (over the objections of some experts on nomenclature). Preparation involves the alcohol, *p*-toluenesulfonyl chloride, and a base, usually pyridine:

$$ROH + C_7H_7SO_2Cl \xrightarrow[\text{solution}]{C_5H_5N} ROSO_2C_7H_7 + C_5H_5\overset{+}{N}HCl^-$$

The alcohol may be primary or secondary, but not tertiary. Alkyl halides can then result from reaction of a sulfonate ester with an alkali halide in acetone, via the S_N2 mechanism:

$$RCH_2OSO_2C_7H_7 + KI \xrightarrow{\text{acetone}} RI + C_7H_7SO_3^-K^+$$

One alkyl halide can be converted to another by a similar reaction:

$$RCH_2Cl + NaI \xrightarrow{\text{acetone}} RCH_2I + NaCl$$

In this example, sodium chloride is very sparingly soluble in acetone, and the reaction is driven to completion by precipitation of sodium chloride. In principle, it is an equilibrium reaction, and we could, in an appropriate solvent, carry out the reverse reaction too. Normally, the procedure is used to convert alkyl chlorides (the most readily available commercially) to bromides and iodides. A variant of this method is the action of potassium fluoride on an alkyl halide or tosylate in ethylene glycol solution:

$$RCH_2Br + KF \longrightarrow RCH_2F + KBr$$

Good procedures for the preparation of alkyl fluorides are scarce. This one has the virtue of avoiding use of the corrosive and unpleasant hydrofluoric acid.

These syntheses of alkyl halides by displacements are shown with primary reactants as examples to emphasize their limitations. They can be used with secondary reactants as well (though yields are poorer), but cannot be used at all with tertiary ones.

A very common S_N2 reaction is the Williamson synthesis of ethers. A sodium or potassium alkoxide reacts with an alkyl halide:

$$RONa + R'X \longrightarrow ROR' + NaX$$

The reaction is often performed by dissolving sodium metal in an excess of the alcohol and then adding the alkyl halide. Sodium salts of phenols, as well as of alcohols, react:

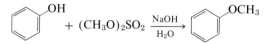

Sulfonate or sulfate esters also react. A common procedure for methylating phenols uses methyl sulfate:

In preparation of unsymmetrical ethers, the less branched alkyl group should be in the alkyl halide. t-Butyl methyl ether should be made from

$$(CH_3)_3CO^-K^+ + CH_3Br \longrightarrow (CH_3)_3COCH_3 + KBr$$

and *not* from methoxide ion and t-butyl bromide, for the obvious reason that tertiary halides are very poor in S_N2 reactions. For similar reasons, we would not try to use the very unreactive aromatic halides.

Preparation of ethers from alcohols and sulfuric acid is somewhat similar. Ethyl hydrogen sulfate is undoubtedly an intermediate in the standard procedure for making diethyl ether:

$$C_2H_5OH + H_2SO_4 \longrightarrow C_2H_5OSO_3H + H_2O$$

$$C_2H_5OH + C_2H_5OSO_3H \longrightarrow C_2H_5OC_2H_5 + H_2SO_4$$

With tertiary alcohols, a carbonium ion mechanism results:

$$(CH_3)_3COH + H^+ \xrightarrow{C_2H_5OH} (CH_3)_3C^+ + H_2O$$

$$(CH_3)_3C^+ + C_2H_5OH \longrightarrow (CH_3)_3COC_2H_5 + H^+$$

Once formed, most ethers are relatively unreactive, a fact which makes them useful as solvents for a variety of organic reactions. They are inert to all common bases and nucleophiles. They can be used as solvents for most organometallic compounds, even though many of these are very powerful bases. (t-Butyllithium does slowly attack diethyl ether in an elimination reaction that yields ethylene.)

Coordination of the unshared pair of electrons on the ether oxygen with a proton or other acid increases the susceptibility of ethers to S_N1 and S_N2 reactions. The most common procedure for cleavage of ethers utilizes concentrated hydriodic acid:

$$ROR + HI \longrightarrow RI + ROH$$

$$ROH + HI \longrightarrow RI + H_2O$$

The reaction involves protonation of the ether, followed by an S_N1 or S_N2 reaction of the protonated species:

$$ROR + H^+ \rightleftharpoons \overset{H^+}{ROR}$$

$$\overset{H^+}{ROR} + I^- \longrightarrow RI + ROH$$

or

$$\overset{H^+}{ROR} \longrightarrow R^+ + ROH$$

$$R^+ + I^- \longrightarrow RI$$

The initial products are an alkyl iodide and an alcohol, though the reaction conditions may be strenuous enough to convert the alcohol to alkyl iodide as well.

The Zeisel method of determining alkoxyl (RO) groups in organic compounds utilizes reaction with hydriodic acid. The alkyl iodides formed are distilled. The final steps are hydrolysis of the alkyl iodides and determination of the liberated iodide ion by reaction with silver nitrate.

A variety of other acid catalysts may be used to cleave ethers. A mixture of concentrated hydrobromic acid and acetic acid is often used. It yields alkyl bromides instead of iodides, of course. Lewis acids such as aluminum chloride, aluminum bromide and zinc chloride have been used. A typical example is:

$$\underset{\underset{O}{\underset{|}{CH_2}}\underset{\diagdown}{\overset{|}{\diagup}}\overset{CH_2-CH_2}{\underset{CH_2}{|}}} {} + C_6H_5\overset{O}{\overset{\|}{C}}Cl \xrightarrow{ZnCl_2} C_6H_5\overset{O}{\overset{\|}{C}}OCH_2CH_2CH_2CH_2Cl$$

Reactivity increases with branching of the alkyl groups, presumably because this facilitates S_N1 cleavage of the protonated ether. Rates of cleavage for ROR′ run: tertiary-primary > secondary-primary > primary-primary. If both groups attached to oxygen are aromatic (as in diphenyl ether, $C_6H_5OC_6H_5$), acid-catalyzed cleavage is impossible. If one group is aliphatic and the other aromatic, reaction will occur:

$$C_6H_5OCH_3 + HBr \xrightarrow{CH_3COOH} C_6H_5OH + CH_3Br$$

Note that the aromatic group is *not* converted to a halide. Aromatic compounds are extremely reluctant to undergo displacement reactions, except under certain special circumstances that will not be discussed here.

One class of ethers does not fit the generalizations we have stated about the difficulty of cleaving the carbon-oxygen bond of an ether. These are the *epoxides,* three-membered cyclic ethers:

$$R-\underset{\underset{O}{\diagdown\diagup}}{CH}-CH-R$$

Apparently the strain in the three-membered ring (bond angles of 60° instead of the normal 109°28′) is sufficient to increase greatly the rate of cleavage.

Acid-catalyzed opening of epoxides occurs much more readily than of ordinary ethers. Relatively dilute aqueous or alcoholic solutions of acid suffice:

$$CH_2\text{---}CH_2 + H_2O \xrightarrow{H^+} HOCH_2CH_2OH$$

$$CH_2\text{---}CH_2 + C_2H_5OH \xrightarrow{H^+} C_2H_5OCH_2CH_2OH$$

The product of the second reaction is one of a class of solvents called *Cellosolves,* which can be made from a variety of alcohols. Because the molecules contain both alcohol and ether functions, they will dissolve an unusually wide range of organic compounds.

The acid-catalyzed ring openings probably involve displacement by a solvent molecule on a protonated epoxide molecule:

$$H_2O + CH_2\text{---}CH_2 \longrightarrow H_2\overset{+}{O}CH_2CH_2OH$$

Where one carbon is secondary or tertiary, the opening may be S_N1 rather than S_N2. In fact, unsymmetrical epoxides give the product from opening of the ring, so as to give the more stable carbonium ion:

$$(CH_3)_2C\text{---}CH_2 \xrightarrow{H^+} [(CH_3)_2\overset{+}{C}\text{---}CH_2OH] \xrightarrow{CH_3OH}$$

$$(CH_3)_2C\text{---}CH_2OH \quad \left(not \quad (CH_3)_2C\text{---}CH_2OCH_3 \right)$$
$$\quad\quad \overset{|}{OCH_3} \quad\quad\quad\quad\quad\quad\quad \overset{|}{OH}$$

The reactivity of epoxides shows up most dramatically in displacements without acid catalysts, conditions under which ordinary ethers are essentially inert. Epoxides can be opened by any of a number of good nucleophiles. Some examples are:

$$CH_2\text{---}CH_2 \xrightarrow[H_2O]{KI} CH_2\text{---}CH_2$$
$$\quad\quad\quad\quad\quad\quad\quad\quad\quad\quad \overset{|}{I} \quad\, \overset{|}{OH}$$

$$CH_2\text{---}CH_2 \xrightarrow{NH_3} CH_2\text{---}CH_2$$
$$\quad\quad\quad\quad\quad\quad\quad\quad\quad\quad \overset{|}{NH_2} \,\overset{|}{OH}$$

$$CH_2\text{---}CH_2 \xrightarrow[H_2O]{KCN} CH_2\text{---}CH_2$$
$$\quad\quad\quad\quad\quad\quad\quad\quad\quad\quad \overset{|}{CN} \,\overset{|}{OH}$$

A particularly useful reaction is that with the Grignard reagent, $RMgX$, which behaves as if it were R^- and MgX^+:

$$CH_2\text{—}CH_2 + RMgX \longrightarrow RCH_2CH_2OMgX$$
$$\underset{O}{\diagdown\diagup}$$

$$RCH_2CH_2OMgX + H_2O \longrightarrow RCH_2CH_2OH + Mg(OH)X$$

This reaction is a good way of increasing the length of a chain by two carbon atoms. More will be said about Grignard reagents in Chap. 7.

One common synthesis of epoxides is itself a displacement reaction. A 2-halo alcohol is treated with base: this converts it to the alkoxide, which then performs an internal displacement:

$$HOCH_2CH_2Cl + OH^- \rightleftharpoons \bar{O}CH_2CH_2Cl + H_2O$$

$$\underset{\underset{Cl}{|}}{\overset{O^-}{\underset{|}{CH_2\text{—}CH_2}}} \longrightarrow \underset{O}{CH_2\text{—}CH_2} + Cl^-$$

The other important synthesis of epoxides is oxidation of an olefin with a peroxy acid:

$$RCH{=}CHR + C_6H_5\overset{O}{\overset{\|}{C}}\text{—}O\text{—}OH \longrightarrow \underset{O}{RCH\text{—}CHR} + C_6H_5\overset{O}{\overset{\|}{C}}\text{—}OH$$

Now that we have seen most of the common types of compounds that undergo S_N2 displacements, we can discuss further examples of these reactions. Unless otherwise noted, the RX used below is an alkyl halide or sulfonate ester, though epoxides will also undergo many of the reactions given. In addition, keep in mind that the best results are obtained when R is primary, and that the reaction usually fails when R is tertiary.

In addition to ordinary ethers and alcohols, thioethers and thioalcohols (mercaptans) may be made by displacement reactions:

$$RX + NaSH \longrightarrow RSH + NaX$$

$$RX + R'SNa \longrightarrow RSR' + NaX$$

Many sulfur-containing nucleophiles are very reactive in S_N2 reactions. Some additional examples are:

$$RX + Na_2SO_3 \longrightarrow RSO_3Na + NaX$$

$$RX + S{=}C(NH_2)_2 \longrightarrow RS\overset{\overset{+}{NH_2}}{\underset{NH_2}{C}}\quad X^-$$

$$[RSC(NH_2)_2]^+X^- \xrightarrow[H_2O]{NaOH} RSH + H_2NCN$$

$$RX + NaSCN \longrightarrow RSCN + NaX$$

The second reaction, that with thiourea, is often preferable to direct reaction with NaSH for mercaptan synthesis, for in this case there is no chance that the mercaptan will alkylate further to a thioether.

Ammonia and amines constitute another important class of nucleophiles. Since nitrogen can form up to four covalent bonds, reaction of ammonia with alkyl halides can occur in a succession of steps:

$$RX + NH_3 \longrightarrow RNH_3^+X^-$$

$$RNH_3^+X^- + NH_3 \longrightarrow RNH_2 + NH_4^+X^-$$

Alkylation of the primary amine gives a secondary amine:

$$R_2NH + RX \longrightarrow R_2NH_2^+X^-$$

$$R_2NH_2^+X^- + RNH_2 \longrightarrow R_2NH + RNH_3^+X^-$$

The secondary amine can give in turn a tertiary amine:

$$R_2NH + RX \longrightarrow R_3NH^+X^-$$

$$R_3NH^+X^- + R_2NH \longrightarrow R_3N + R_2NH_2^+X^-$$

Finally, the tertiary amine can give a tetraalkylammonium salt:

$$R_3N + RX \longrightarrow R_4N^+X^-$$

When ammonia is mixed with an alkyl halide, any or all of these reactions can occur. Primary amine can be favored by a large excess of ammonia. Yields of the more highly substituted amines increase as the proportion of ammonia is diminished. If an insufficient excess of ammonia is present, some of the amine is still present as its salt with HX, and may be completely liberated by treatment with sodium hydroxide:

$$R_3NH^+X^- + NaOH \longrightarrow R_3N + NaX + H_2O$$

This is usually done in any case, to avoid loss of any amine in salt form.

Though some control may be exerted over the relative yields of primary, secondary and tertiary amines as noted above, completely pure preparations of any one amine cannot be achieved by this method. Another displacement reaction that does yield pure primary amine is the *Gabriel synthesis*, which starts with the potassium salt of phthalimide:

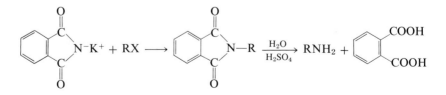

Sodium cyanamide is the starting material in one method of preparing pure secondary amines:

$$2RX + Na_2^+ \begin{bmatrix} \overset{=}{N}-C\equiv N \\ \Updownarrow \\ \overset{-}{N}=C=\overset{-}{N} \end{bmatrix} \longrightarrow R_2N-C\equiv N + 2NaX$$

$$R_2N-C\equiv N + 2H_2O \xrightarrow[OH^-]{H^+ \text{ or}} R_2NH + CO_2 + NH_3$$

Alkylation of secondary amines by alkyl halides gives tertiary amine plus tetraalkylammonium salt, but these can be separated easily because one is ionic and the other not.

Esters of carboxylic acids can be prepared by substitution reactions. An example is an alkyl halide with sodium acetate:

$$RX + CH_3CO_2^-Na^+ \longrightarrow RO\overset{\overset{\displaystyle O}{\|}}{C}CH_3 + NaX$$

This is an S_N2 reaction and occurs with inversion.

Another method of obtaining carboxylic esters is *solvolysis* (reaction with solvent) of an alkyl halide or sulfonate ester in the corresponding carboxylic acid. Acetic and formic acids are the solvents most often used. Some examples are:

$$CH_3CH_2Br + HCO_2H \longrightarrow CH_3CH_2O\overset{\overset{\displaystyle O}{\|}}{C}H + HBr$$

$$(CH_3)_2CHOSO_2C_7H_7 + CH_3CO_2H \longrightarrow (CH_3)_2CHO\overset{\overset{\displaystyle O}{\|}}{C}CH_3 + C_7H_7SO_3H$$

In some cases the strong acid which is liberated (HBr or $C_7H_7SO_3H$ in these examples) may attack the product. To neutralize the acid, an equivalent of the conjugate base of the solvent (formate or acetate ions as their sodium salts) is often added:

$$HBr + HCO_2^-Na^+ \longrightarrow HCO_2H + NaBr$$

Most of these solvolyses are S_N1 reactions with carbonium ions or ion pairs as intermediates (see earlier discussion of the S_N1 mechanism), though the solvolysis of a primary halide is better described as an S_N2 reaction with a solvent molecule functioning as nucleophile.

Solvolyses are by no means limited to those in carboxylic acid solution. The hydrolysis of alkyl halides to alcohols mentioned earlier is a special case of solvolysis. Pure water can be used, whereas mixtures of water and miscible solvents, such as acetone or dioxane, are more advantageous for less soluble substances. Solvolyses in alcohol solution yield ethers:

$$RX + CH_3CH_2OH \longrightarrow ROCH_2CH_3 + HX$$

Alcohol-water mixtures are undesirable in synthetic applications, as they produce some ROH in addition to the ether.

The final nucleophilic displacements to be covered are those resulting in formation of carbon-carbon bonds. These are of particular importance in organic synthesis. (We have already seen a few examples: the formation of alkyl cyanides and the reaction of Grignard reagents with ethylene oxide.) Two of the most important nucleophiles are derived from aceto-acetic ester and malonic ester.†

Acetoacetic ester reacts with a base (usually ethoxide ion) to lose a proton from its methylene group. The charge is spread over two atoms, carbon and oxygen, and the anion is said to be *ambident:*

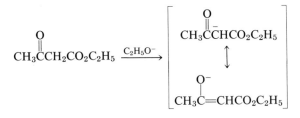

Reaction with an ordinary primary alkyl halide results in reaction entirely at carbon, though "O-alkylation" can compete successfully with "C-alky-lation" when the reactant is prone to react by an S_N1 mechanism (CH_3OCH_2Cl is an example). With simple alkyl halides O-alkylation is seldom a problem. Tertiary halides do not alkylate at all. They undergo elimination reactions (Chap. 4) instead.

The normal C-alkylation is:

$$CH_3\overset{O}{\overset{\|}{C}}\overset{-}{C}HCO_2C_2H_5 + RX \longrightarrow CH_3\overset{O}{\overset{\|}{C}}-\underset{R}{C}HCO_2C_2H_5$$

The product still has one ionizable hydrogen and can alkylate again:

$$CH_3\overset{O}{\overset{\|}{C}}-\underset{R}{\overset{-}{C}}CO_2C_2H_5 + RX \longrightarrow CH_3\overset{O}{\overset{\|}{C}}-\underset{R}{\overset{R}{C}}CO_2C_2H_5$$

† Also discussed in C. D. Gutsche, *op. cit.*

The synthetic utility of the reaction becomes more apparent when we see the results of hydrolyzing the alkylated ester:

$$CH_3\overset{\overset{O}{\|}}{C}-\overset{\overset{R}{|}}{\underset{\underset{R}{|}}{C}}-CO_2C_2H_5 + H_2O \xrightarrow{H^+} \left[CH_3\overset{\overset{O}{\|}}{C}-\overset{\overset{R}{|}}{\underset{\underset{R}{|}}{C}}-CO_2H \right] \longrightarrow CH_3\overset{\overset{O}{\|}}{C}-\overset{\overset{R}{|}}{\underset{\underset{R}{|}}{C}}H + CO_2$$

The acid formed is unstable and *decarboxylates* under the conditions of hydrolysis to yield a ketone. The monoalkylated ester would give CH_3COCH_2R. We can therefore prepare a wide variety of ketones from acetoacetic ester.

Malonic ester behaves in a closely analogous fashion:

$$CH_2(CO_2C_2H_5)_2 + C_2H_5O^- \longrightarrow \overset{-}{C}H(CO_2C_2H_5)_2$$

$$\overset{-}{C}H(CO_2C_2H_5)_2 + RX \longrightarrow RCH(CO_2C_2H_5)_2$$

$$RCH(CO_2C_2H_5)_2 + C_2H_5O^- \longrightarrow R\overset{-}{C}(CO_2C_2H_5)_2$$

$$R\overset{-}{C}(CO_2C_2H_5)_2 + RX \longrightarrow R_2C(CO_2C_2H_5)_2$$

Appropriate choice of conditions permits stopping at monoalkylation. Hydrolysis yields the corresponding malonic acid:

$$R_2C(CO_2C_2H_5)_2 + H_2O \xrightarrow{H^+} R_2C(COOH)_2$$

The acid is stable at room temperature, but decarboxylates when heated to about 140°:

$$R_2C(COOH)_2 \xrightarrow{heat} R_2CHCOOH + CO_2$$

The sequence of reactions thus constitutes a synthesis of substituted acetic acids.

Many variants on both the malonic and acetoacetic ester syntheses have been reported. One is the use of a *dihalide* to form a cyclic compound:

$$CH_2(COOC_2H_5)_2 \xrightarrow[Br[CH_2]_3Br]{C_2H_5O^-} \underset{\underset{(CH_2)_3Br}{|}}{C}H(COOC_2H_5)_2 \xrightarrow{C_2H_5O^-}$$

$$\overset{CH_2}{\underset{CH_2}{\overset{|}{\diagdown}}}\overset{}{\underset{}{C(COOC_2H_5)_2}} \xrightarrow[\text{(2) heat}]{\text{(1) H}^+,\text{ H}_2\text{O}} \overset{CH_2}{\underset{CH_2}{\overset{|}{\diagdown}}}CHCOOH$$

cyclobutanecarboxylic acid

Note that the first-formed product undergoes an *internal* S_N2 displacement of the remaining bromine atom to close the ring.

Another method of forming carbon-carbon bonds starts with an acetylene. Hydrogen attached to a triply-bonded carbon is acidic enough to be removed by a very strong base, such as sodium amide in liquid ammonia:

$$HC\equiv CH + NH_2^- \xrightarrow{NH_3} HC\equiv C^- + NH_3$$

The resulting anion can then react with an alkyl halide:

$$HC\equiv C^- + RX \longrightarrow HC\equiv CR + X^-$$

The process can be repeated to alkylate the other end of the triple bond:

$$RC\equiv CH + NH_2^- \xrightarrow{NH_3} RC\equiv C^- + NH_3$$

$$RC\equiv C^- + RX \longrightarrow RC\equiv CR + X^-$$

(The second alkyl group, incidentally, need not be the same as the first, neither here nor in the malonic or acetoacetic ester syntheses.)

These reactions provide a starting point for numerous other syntheses, for the alkylated acetylenes can undergo further reactions: among these are hydrogenation to olefins or unsaturated hydrocarbons, and addition of water to give ketones (see Chap. 2).

CHAPTER 3 REVIEW QUESTIONS

1. Define: leaving group, concerted reaction, ion pair, 1,2-shift, I-strain, S_N2 reaction.

2. Under what conditions, and with what types of reactants, are S_N1 reactions favored?

3. Why does $(C_6H_5)_2CHBr$ hydrolyze more slowly in the presence of added LiBr?

4. Explain the order of reactivities observed in the Lucas test.

5. List as many methods as you can for the synthesis of alkyl chlorides.

6. Explain why epoxides are much more reactive toward displacements than are open-chain ethers.

7. What would you expect to be the rate of solvolysis of t-butyl chloride in each of the following solvents, relative to the rate in ethanol (simply specify *faster* or *slower*): acetic acid, 90% acetone-10% water, 50% ethanol-50% water, t-butyl alcohol?

8. Using n-propyl bromide, plus any other necessary reagents, devise syntheses of the following compounds:

(a) $CH_3CH_2CH_2NH_2$ (pure)   (b) $CH_3CH_2CH_2CH_2COOH$

(c) $CH_3COCH_2CH_2CH_2CH_3$ (d) $CH_3CH_2CH_2C\equiv CH$

4
Elimination Reactions

4.1 DEFINITIONS AND EXAMPLES

An elimination reaction is said to occur when two atoms or groups attached to adjacent carbon atoms are lost:

$$
\begin{array}{c}
\text{H} \quad \text{H} \\
\text{H}-\overset{|}{\underset{|}{\text{C}}}-\overset{|}{\underset{|}{\text{C}}}-\text{H} \\
\text{X} \quad \text{Y}
\end{array}
\longrightarrow
\begin{array}{c}
\text{H} \\
\diagdown \\
\text{C}{=}\text{C} \\
\diagup \\
\text{H}
\end{array}
\begin{array}{c}
\text{H} \\
\diagup \\
\\
\diagdown \\
\text{H}
\end{array}
+ \text{X} + \text{Y}
$$

The result of this process is the formation of a double bond between the two carbon atoms. Reactions in which the two atoms, or groups, are not on adjacent carbon atoms are sometimes called elimination reactions, but such reactions are less common and usually do not lead to olefins. We will restrict ourselves to 1,2-eliminations whose products are olefins.

Among concrete examples of these are:

$$\text{CH}_3\underset{\underset{\text{Br}}{|}}{\text{CHCH}_3} + \text{C}_2\text{H}_5\text{O}^- \longrightarrow \text{CH}_3\text{CH}{=}\text{CH}_2 + \text{Br}^- + \text{C}_2\text{H}_5\text{OH}$$

$$\text{CH}_3-\underset{\underset{\text{CH}_3}{|}}{\overset{\overset{\text{CH}_3}{|}}{\text{C}}}-\text{OH} \xrightarrow{\text{H}_2\text{SO}_4} \text{CH}_2{=}\underset{\diagdown \text{CH}_3}{\overset{\diagup \text{CH}_3}{\text{C}}} + \text{H}_2\text{O}$$

$$\text{CH}_3\text{CH}_2\overset{+}{\text{N}}(\text{CH}_3)_3\ \overline{\text{O}}\text{H} \xrightarrow{\text{heat}} \text{CH}_2{=}\text{CH}_2 + \text{N}(\text{CH}_3)_3 + \text{H}_2\text{O}$$

In these equations, one of the "leaving groups" is always hydrogen (which departs as a proton); the others are Br^-, OH^- and $\text{N}(\text{CH}_3)_3$, respectively. Though one of the leaving groups is hydrogen in nearly all elimination reactions, there are some reactions where this is not so:

$$\text{BrCH}_2\text{CH}_2\text{Br} + \text{Zn} \longrightarrow \text{CH}_2{=}\text{CH}_2 + \text{ZnBr}_2$$

These examples illustrate the wide variety of starting materials that can be used for olefin-forming eliminations. A more thorough discussion of synthetic applications will be given at the end of this chapter.

4.2 THE E1 AND E2 MECHANISMS

Most elimination reactions are now believed to occur by either of two important mechanisms. These are the *E1* (elimination, unimolecular) and *E2* (elimination, bimolecular) *mechanisms*. The terminology, and much

of our knowledge of these mechanisms as well, is due to E. D. Hughes†
and C. K. Ingold.

The E1 mechanism requires only that the reactant be placed in an
ionizing solvent. This leads to the formation of a carbonium ion which
then loses a proton to complete the process:

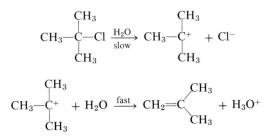

The rate-determining step of the reaction is formation of the carbonium
ion. The term E1 arises from the fact that this step is unimolecular, requir-
ing no added reagent (except the solvent) to promote loss of the leaving
group (Cl^- in our example). The intermediate carbonium ion is, of course,
the same as that in the S_N1 reaction (Chap. 3); in fact, S_N1 and E1 reactions usually occur simultaneously. The conditions under which one or
the other can be expected to predominate will be discussed in Chap. 5.

The other major mechanism, E2, requires the presence of a base before
it will occur. Unlike the E1 reaction, it seems to occur in a single step
without any intermediates. The mechanism and the approximate nature
of the transition state are illustrated in the following reaction of potassium
ethoxide with isopropyl bromide:

$$C_2H_5O^- + H-CH_2-\underset{\underset{CH_3}{|}}{CH}-Br \longrightarrow \left[C_2H_5O\text{---}H\text{---}CH_2=\underset{\underset{CH_3}{|}}{CH}\text{---}Br \right]^- \longrightarrow$$

transition state

$$C_2H_5OH + CH_2=\underset{\underset{CH_3}{|}}{CH} + Br^-$$

Substitution by the S_N2 mechanism may occur under the same conditions,
just as with the E1 and S_N1 reactions; this competition will also be discussed in Chap. 5. For the present, we will limit ourselves to the ranges
of applicability and the consequences of the two elimination mechanisms.

Our descriptions of the E1 and E2 reactions should be put on a more
quantitative basis before we proceed. The rate of a unimolecular reaction

† E. D. Hughes, 1906–1963. English. Engaged in a long and very fruitful collaboration with
C. K. Ingold (see footnote, p. 33, for a biographical sketch) on the mechanisms of substitution and elimination reactions.

depends on the first power of the concentration of the reactant. Thus, in our example

$$\text{rate} = k_1[(CH_3)_3CCl]$$

A bimolecular reaction, on the other hand, has a rate proportional to the concentrations of both reactants. Using the foregoing example of the E2 reaction,

$$\text{rate} = k_2[(CH_3)_2CHBr][C_2H_5O^-]$$

A bimolecular reaction may not always obey a *second-order* rate law (one in which the rate is proportional to the products of two concentrations, or to the square of one). If one reactant is present in great excess, its concentration will remain constant during the reaction. Assuming we use a large excess of base,

$$k_2[C_2H_5O^-] = k'$$

and

$$\text{rate} = k'[(CH_3)_2CHBr]$$

in which case the reaction is said to be *pseudo-unimolecular*. A more fundamental source of confusion is the fact that two or more different mechanisms may satisfy the same rate law.

4.3 THE E1cb, OR CARBANION, MECHANISM

Let us assume that the reaction of isopropyl bromide with ethoxide ion occurs in the following two stages:

$$C_2H_5O^- + CH_3\underset{Br}{CHCH_3} \overset{\text{fast}}{\rightleftharpoons} \overset{-}{C}H_2\underset{Br}{CHCH_3} + C_2H_5OH$$

$$\overset{-}{C}H_2\underset{Br}{CHCH_3} \overset{\text{slow}}{\longrightarrow} CH_2{=}CHCH_3 + Br^-$$

The overall rate is limited to that of the slower (rate-determining) second stage, which depends only on the concentration of the anion (the *conjugate base* of isopropyl bromide). The concentration of the anion is governed by an equilibrium:

$$K = \frac{[\text{anion}]}{[(CH_3)_2CHBr][C_2H_5O^-]}$$

The concentration of ethyl alcohol, the solvent, remains constant and thus need not appear in the equilibrium expression. The rate of reaction then is given by:

$$\text{rate} = k_2[\text{anion}] = k_2K[(CH_3)_2CHBr][C_2H_5O^-]$$

which is the same as the rate law for the E2 reaction, except for the significance of the proportionality constant. This has been called the *E1cb mechanism* (elimination, unimolecular from the conjugate base of the reactant).

A distinction between these two mechanisms can be made by means of tracer experiments. Suppose we use, as solvent, ethyl alcohol in which the hydrogen attached to the oxygen is replaced by the heavy isotope deuterium. Any of the intermediate anions that pick up protons to go back to isopropyl bromide will have a much greater chance of picking them up from a deuterated solvent molecule than from the normal ethyl alcohol produced in the first stage. The reaction will be:

$$\overset{-}{C}H_2CHCH_3 + C_2H_5OD \longrightarrow DCH_2CHCH_3 + C_2H_5O^-$$
$$\quad\ \ |\qquad\qquad\qquad\qquad\qquad\qquad\quad\ |$$
$$\quad\ \ Br\qquad\qquad\qquad\qquad\qquad\qquad\ Br$$

If we were to recover isopropyl bromide from the reaction mixture before all of it had reacted, we would find that it contained deuterium—if the E1cb mechanism were correct. The single-stage E2 mechanism offers no opportunity for incorporation of deuterium. This experiment has not been performed on isopropyl bromide itself, but with closely similar compounds a failure to incorporate deuterium argues for the correctness of the E2 mechanism.

Only under rather special circumstances does the E1cb reaction seem to occur. For example, the carbon-fluorine bond is very strong, and the following exchange reaction has been found to be faster than the elimination of HF from the reactant:

$$CHCl_2CF_3 + D_2O \overset{NaOD}{\rightleftharpoons} CDCl_2CF_3 + HOD$$

Evidently a proton is removed by the base to give $^-CCl_2CF_3$, which picks up a deuteron from the solvent (D_2O) faster than it loses fluoride ion.

4.4 CYCLIC ELIMINATIONS

The last important mechanistic classification of elimination reactions is that of *cyclic eliminations*. These are unimolecular elimination reactions that occur in a single step (unlike the E1 reaction), in which the leaving group removes the β proton as it departs. Most of these are *pyrolytic* reactions (reactions brought about by heating the reactant), and many of them occur in the vapor phase. Some important examples are:

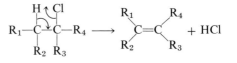

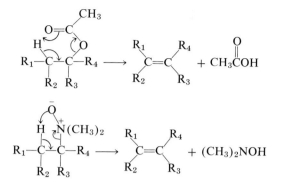

The curved arrows in the formulas represent the shifts of electron pairs that occur during the reaction. These intramolecular mechanisms are not, strictly speaking, ionic reactions, as no free ions are involved at any time. Some similarities to ionic reactions in behavior may be noted in certain cases. The pyrolysis of alkyl halides, for example, shows a dependence of structure on reactivity similar to that of E1 reactions. It is most unlikely that free carbonium ions could exist in the vapor phase, so this parallelism probably means simply that the transition state bears some resemblance to an ion pair R^+Cl^-.

4.5 STEREOCHEMISTRY OF ELIMINATION REACTIONS

A point of interest in many applications of elimination reactions is their *stereochemistry;* i.e., the manner in which the atoms are oriented with respect to each other in the transition state. If we sight along the carbon-carbon bond of isopropyl bromide, the two extreme possibilities for the positions of the groups attached to the two carbons are

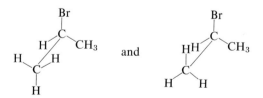

We call these the *staggered* and *eclipsed* conformations, respectively (see Allinger, *op. cit.*). These can be interconverted easily by rotation about the carbon-carbon bond, and this rotation is much faster than any re-action of the compound. Once the base has attacked a hydrogen on the methyl group and the formation of the double bond has started, rotation is no longer free. The carbon-hydrogen and carbon-bromine bonds that are being broken will then be oriented in a specific fashion with respect to each other. In our example, isopropyl bromide, we have no way of telling what this orientation is, for the only possible product is propylene regardless of which hydrogen is lost.

When rotation about the carbon-carbon bond of the reactant is restricted, the hydrogens to be lost are no longer equivalent and determination of the stereochemistry of the reaction becomes possible. One way to accomplish this is to start with an unsaturated halide. Chloromaleic acid (H and Cl *cis*) and chlorofumaric acid (H and Cl *trans*) both give acetylenedicarboxylic acid on treatment with base; but chlorofumaric acid reacts about fifty times faster:

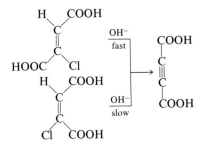

Thus the E2 reaction seems to be easier when the hydrogen and the leaving group are *trans* and the four atoms involved (here H—C—C—Cl) are in the same plane.

This evidence is not completely convincing, for we have no assurance that unsaturated halides will behave in the same way as the saturated halides that one encounters more frequently in the E2 reaction. A way around this objection is provided by a study of the reactions of cyclic halides, where rotation about carbon-carbon single bonds is restricted by the ring structure. There are thus two isomers of 2-alkylcyclohexyl halides. One of these has hydrogen *trans* to the halogen on both of the carbons adjacent to the one which bears the halogen. The other has only one *trans* hydrogen, the alkyl group occupying the other *trans* position. The results when these two isomers are treated with base are:

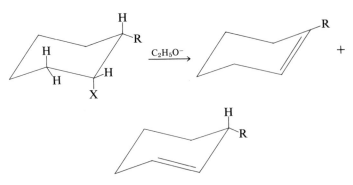

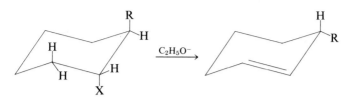

Loss of a hydrogen *trans* to the halogen is again favored, and the stereochemical preference shown by unsaturated halides is therefore general. In fact, leaving groups other than the halogens usually give the same *trans* stereochemistry. These include OSO_2R (esters of sulfonic acids) and NR_3 (tetraalkylammonium salts).

A final demonstration of the stereochemistry of E2 reactions is found with open-chain compounds which possess two or more asymmetric carbons, and hence are capable of existing as *diastereomers*. Certain 1,2-dihalides fall into this category. The products obtained in E2 reactions of these compounds depend upon the stereochemistry of the starting material:

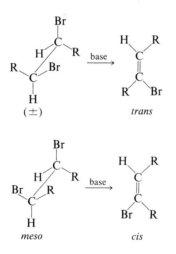

The ($\pm$)-dibromide can have hydrogen and bromine *trans* only when the two R groups are also *trans*, and so must give *trans* olefin. Similarly, the *meso* isomer can give only *cis* olefin in a *trans* elimination of H and Br. Exactly the reverse of these two results would have been found if the H and Br had been *cis* to each other in the transition state.

The preference for *trans* elimination does not always hold. The E2 reaction of *trans*-2-phenylcyclohexyltrimethylammonium hydroxide (H and $N(CH_3)_3$ *cis*) gives 1-phenylcyclohexene, in spite of the fact that a *trans* hydrogen could be lost (to give 3-phenylcyclohexene):

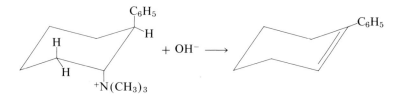

The reason seems to be that a phenyl group on the β-carbon usually accelerates E2 reactions rather strongly, for reasons that we will discuss in Chap. 6. In the reaction pictured above it speeds up the normally-slow *cis* elimination so much that it goes faster than the *trans* elimination. The other β-carbon does not bear a phenyl group, so elimination toward it presumably proceeds at about the same rate as it would in the unsubstituted cyclohexyltrimethylammonium hydroxide. Violations of the *trans* rule of elimination are noted with some other strongly-accelerating substituents on the β-carbon.

Certain "bridged-ring" compounds also violate the *trans* rule. In the 2,3-dichloronorboranes, *cis* elimination of H and Cl is actually somewhat faster:

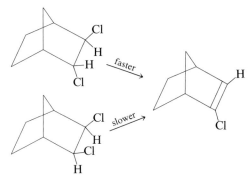

Here the bridged, cage-like structure holds all of the atoms very rigidly in place. The atoms H—C—C—Cl cannot become coplanar in the second isomer, even though they are *trans*. This is evidence for the unproved statement made earlier that a *trans coplanar* arrangement of the four atoms involved was necessary for an easy E2 reaction. These results suggest that coplanarity can be at least as important as the *trans* orientation, for the *cis* H and Cl in the faster-reacting isomer are coplanar.

A brief comment on the reasons behind the stereochemistry of E2 reactions is in order: We know that the π orbital of a carbon-carbon double bond is formed by the overlap of two p orbitals on the two carbons. If these p orbitals are to overlap most effectively, they must be parallel to each other. Now, an elimination reaction can be regarded as producing two p orbitals from what were the bonds to the leaving group and the β-hydrogen, respectively. If the p orbitals are to be parallel, these two bonds must be parallel too. This would be true for a *trans* and staggered conformation, or a *cis* and eclipsed conformation:

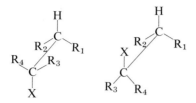

Staggered conformations are favored over eclipsed conformations because steric strain is less, and this may be part of the reason for the normal *trans* preference. Where the groups are constrained to an eclipsed conformation, as in the bridged-ring compounds above, the *cis* elimination is actually favored. Another argument that has been used for *trans* elimination views the electrons of the carbon-hydrogen bond as "displacing" the leaving group. By analogy to the S_N2 reaction, this should be easier when they attack the back of the α-carbon.

The E1 reaction shows less stereochemical preference than the E2 reaction. A simple picture (see the following diagram) would predict it to show none at all. The groups attached to the intermediate carbonium ion are in a plane, and the distinction between *cis* and *trans* disappears because the two sides of the plane are equivalent. Thus, *cis* and *trans* isomers of a 2-alkylcyclohexyl chloride would be expected to yield the same carbonium ion, and hence the same mixture of olefins, under E1 conditions:

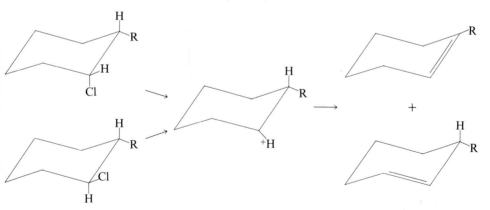

In fact, the 1-alkylcyclohexene is favored with either isomer, but more of it results from the *cis* isomer, where it results from *trans* loss of H and Cl. The explanation is undoubtedly similar to that for preferred inversion in S_N1 reactions. Apparently the carbonium ion is partially shielded by the departing group, or unsymmetrically solvated. It thus has some "memory" of the isomer from which it was obtained and, by analogy to the E2 reaction, prefers *trans* elimination. This is not usually a very marked preference, compared to that in the E2 reaction.

The stereochemistry of eliminations by the cyclic mechanism is easy to predict. The leaving group and the β-hydrogen must obviously be *cis* to each other if the cyclic transition state is to be formed:

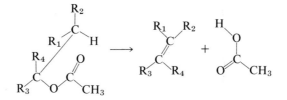

The reaction thus occurs through an eclipsed conformation, and the groups that are *cis* to each other in this conformation will be *cis* in the olefin as well.

4.6 PRODUCT RATIOS; RULES OF SAYTZEV AND HOFMANN

The influence of structure on reactivity can be considered in two connections. We can examine the relative rates of reaction of different reactants, or we can examine the proportions of products when a single reactant can react by two or more paths. The relative reactivities of different compounds in elimination reactions are important in deciding whether substitution or elimination will predominate in a given case. This aspect of reactivity will be discussed more fully in Chap. 5. Our study of stereochemistry has provided examples of the latter approach. The ratio of % 1-alkylcyclohexene to % 3-alkylcyclohexene from a 2-alkylcyclohexyl halide is simply the ratio of rates of elimination into the two possible branches (toward the alkyl group or away from it). In the example cited, the product ratio is determined mainly by stereochemistry. In open-chain reactants where stereochemistry is not decisive, the product proportions are a measure of the intrinsic relative reactivities of the two branches. We can thus obtain the same type of information from product ratios as we can by measuring rates of reaction with different substances.

In practice, we find it more often necessary to consider product ratios. If a particular reactant undergoes an elimination too slowly, we can usually just raise the temperature, or start over again with a more reactive substance. A much more subtle grasp of theory is needed to choose a reaction that will yield a preponderance of the desired isomer, for the measures that were successful in making the reaction go at a convenient rate may have an equal effect on elimination in both branches, and so not affect the product ratio. Fortunately, it is often possible to choose a reactant and the conditions for an elimination reaction so as to obtain a preponderance of the desired product. Just how this is done can best be appreciated after seeing the experimental facts and their mechanistic explanation.

Certain regularities in product proportions were noticed in the last century by Hofmann† and by Saytzev,‡ though the rules that they suggested remained purely empirical for a long time. The *Saytzev rule* as originally worded states that an alkyl halide that can form a double bond into either of two branches will give, preferentially, that olefin having the greater number of alkyl groups attached to the double bond. The rule has become somewhat more complicated as more examples have become available, but most cases are included when we say that it applies to nearly all E2 reactions of alkyl halides, and to E1 reactions regardless of the nature of the leaving group. Some specific examples are:

$$CH_3\underset{\underset{Br}{|}}{C}HCH_2CH_3 + C_2H_5O^- \longrightarrow \underset{81\%}{CH_3CH{=}CHCH_3} + \underset{19\%}{CH_3CH_2CH{=}CH_2}$$

$$CH_3CH_2\underset{\underset{Br}{|}}{\overset{\overset{CH_3}{|}}{C}}CH_3 + C_2H_5O^- \longrightarrow \underset{70\%}{CH_3CH{=}\overset{\overset{CH_3}{|}}{C}CH_3} + \underset{30\%}{CH_3CH_2\overset{\overset{CH_3}{|}}{C}{=}CH_2}$$

$$CH_3CH_2\underset{\underset{{}^+S(CH_3)_2}{|}}{\overset{\overset{CH_3}{|}}{C}}CH_3 + C_2H_5OH \longrightarrow \underset{87\%}{CH_3CH{=}\overset{\overset{CH_3}{|}}{C}CH_3} + \underset{13\%}{CH_3CH_2\overset{\overset{CH_3}{|}}{C}{=}CH_2}$$

The first two of these reactions occur via the E2, and the third via the E1, mechanism. As we shall see later, E2 reactions of sulfonium salts give entirely different results.

Another way of stating the Saytzev rule is to say that the more stable of the possible olefins is formed preferentially. This is not just a question of an equilibrium mixture of products being formed. The conditions of elimination reactions are seldom strenuous enough to isomerize olefins, so the product compositions reflect the relative rates of formation of the products (*kinetic control*). The predominant product will be that which is formed from the transition state of lower energy. Formation of the more stable product in greater amount suggests that the transition state leading to it is stabilized by the same factors that stabilize the product. Such reasoning has led to the belief that transition states for most elimination

† A. W. Hofmann, 1818–1895. German. Professor at the Royal College of Chemistry in London and later at the University of Berlin. Extensive studies of amines and aromatic compounds.
‡ A. N. Saytzev, 1841–1910. Russian. As with other Russian names (Markovnikov, for example), there is no general agreement on the proper transliteration. The original is Зайцев, and common versions are Saytzeff, Zaitsev, Saytzev, etc.

reactions have partial double-bond character. The E2 reaction has a transition state something like this:

base

and the E1 reaction has a transition state something like this:

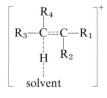

solvent

Note that we discuss orientation in terms of the transition state for loss of a proton by the carbonium ion, rather than the transition state for rate-determining formation of the carbonium ion, for it is the step in which the proton is lost that determines the products.

So far nothing has been said in explanation of the fact that olefins with more alkyl groups on the double bond are more stable. Discussion of this point has been delayed intentionally, since the validity of our explanation of the Saytzev rule does not really depend on it. The important mechanistic point is the conclusion that the transition state has double-bond character. Why a double bond should be stabilized by alkyl substitution is less clear, and has been the subject of considerable controversy. The most widely accepted explanation involves an interaction of the carbon-hydrogen bonds of the alkyl substituent with the π electrons of the double bond. The more alkyl substituents there are, the more such interactions will be possible, and the greater the stabilization resulting from them. This phenomenon, called *hyperconjugation,* will be discussed in Chap. 6.

Some violations of the Saytzev rule are known. Those that arise from changes in the base or in the reaction conditions will be discussed after we have examined the mechanism of elimination reactions in more detail. Apparent violations may result when the more substituted olefin is no longer the more stable, as happens with certain highly-branched olefins. Consider the two isomers

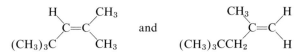

In the first of these, a large group (*t*-butyl) is compelled by the geometry of the olefinic bond to stay in the same plane as a methyl group, and *steric*

strain results from the interactions of these two groups. The second isomer has only hydrogen atoms on one end of the double bond, and steric strain is much less. Consequently, elimination reactions of

$$(CH_3)_3CCH_2\overset{\overset{\displaystyle Br}{|}}{C}(CH_3)_2$$

lead mainly to the second isomer. This "violation" of the Saytzev rule is included in the rule itself by the alternate definition (given above), which predicts the *more stable* product, regardless of whether or not it is also the more substituted product.

From what has been said so far, one might conclude that all elimination reactions should yield the more stable product; this is not so. Certain types of compounds, mainly tetraalkylammonium and trialkylsulfonium salts, show precisely the opposite behavior in E2 reactions. Historically, this behavior was the first to be observed. As originally stated in 1851 (as compared to 1875 for the Saytzev rule), the *Hofmann rule* said that a quaternary ammonium hydroxide containing two or more alkyl groups would lose an ethyl group (as ethylene) in preference to a larger alkyl group. The rule has since been extended to include preferential formation of the *less-substituted* olefin where the choice is between elimination into two different branches of the same alkyl group. Two examples are:

$$CH_3CH_2-\overset{\overset{\displaystyle CH_3}{|}}{\underset{\underset{\displaystyle CH_3}{|}}{N}}\overset{+}{}-CH_2CH_2CH_3 + OH^- \longrightarrow CH_2{=}CH_2 + \overset{\overset{\displaystyle CH_3}{|}}{\underset{\underset{\displaystyle CH_3}{|}}{N}}-CH_2CH_2CH_3$$

$$CH_3CH_2\overset{\overset{\displaystyle }{}}{\underset{\underset{\displaystyle +S(CH_3)_2}{|}}{C}}HCH_3 + C_2H_5O^- \longrightarrow \underset{74\%}{CH_3CH_2CH{=}CH_2} + \underset{26\%}{CH_3CH{=}CHCH_3}$$

We can thus define the Hofmann rule as the antithesis of the Saytzev rule: the favored product in E2 reactions of so-called "onium" salts is the *less stable* olefin.

There is not complete agreement on the cause of this entirely different orientation in reactions which apparently follow the same E2 mechanism as the alkyl halides. A widely accepted and probably correct explanation runs as follows. The carbon-nitrogen and carbon-sulfur bonds in onium salts are more difficult to break than are the carbon-halogen bonds of alkyl halides. Now, when a β-hydrogen is removed as a proton, we can regard the electrons that formerly belonged to the carbon-hydrogen bond as "displacing" the leaving group. If the leaving group is difficult to displace, as is the NR_3^+ group, a rather high electron density must be built up on the β-carbon before the bond between the leaving group and the α-carbon begins to break. The transition state, then, is probably one in which the β-carbon-hydrogen bond is much more nearly broken than is the bond from the α-carbon to the leaving group.

4.7 THE VARIABLE TRANSITION STATE

Reactions having ostensibly the same mechanisms may differ considerably in the extent to which bonds are broken and/or formed in the transition state. The precise balance and timing of the bond-making and bond-breaking processes will depend mainly on the relative strengths of the bonds. The E2 reaction can have a "spectrum" of transition states extending over the following range:

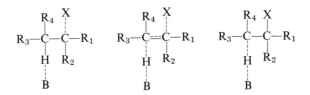

where B represents the attacking base. The central diagram represents the balanced situation presumably involved in reactions following the Saytzev rule, where the transition state has considerable double-bond character and is stabilized by the same factors that stabilize the olefin itself. On the right we have the situation just discussed for onium salts, where the C—X bond remains nearly intact until the C—H bond is almost completely broken. The left-hand diagram represents the opposite extreme, where the C—X bond is so easily broken it needs little help from the electrons of the carbon-hydrogen bond. This is probably the case for reactions that are near the borderline between E2 and E1 reactions.

Returning to the right-hand diagram, the relative lack of C—X cleavage in the transition state means that the electron pair released by removal of the β-hydrogen remains largely localized on the β-carbon. Electron density at the β-position thus increases. Any substituent on the β-carbon that withdraws electrons will help relieve this increase in electron density, while electron-repelling substituents will increase it still further. Alkyl groups are electron-repelling relative to hydrogen, so alkyl substitution will *destabilize* the transition state. At the same time, the virtual absence of double-bond character between the α- and β-carbons means that the beneficial effect on a double bond of alkyl substitution will not be exerted. The more alkyl groups exist on the β-carbon, the more difficult will be the elimination reaction; this is in accord with the Hofmann rule.

4.8 EFFECTS OF SOLVENT AND BASE ON PRODUCT RATIOS

Hofmann-rule behavior has been observed even with alkyl halides, when certain bases are used. H. C. Brown has shown that use of potassium *t*-butoxide in *t*-butyl alcohol leads to larger proportions of the less-substituted olefin than the more usual potassium ethoxide in ethyl alcohol. For example:

$$CH_3CH_2\overset{\overset{\displaystyle CH_3}{|}}{\underset{\underset{\displaystyle Br}{|}}{C}}CH_3 + (CH_3)_3CO^- \longrightarrow \underset{31\%}{CH_3CH=\overset{\overset{\displaystyle CH_3}{|}}{C}CH_3} + \underset{69\%}{CH_3CH_2\overset{\overset{\displaystyle CH_3}{|}}{C}=CH_2}$$

The ratio is almost the exact opposite of that obtained with ethoxide ion! The reason is, again, not entirely settled. Possibly the stronger base, t-butoxide, increases carbanion character at the same time that carbon-bromine cleavage becomes more difficult because of the less polar solvent, t-butyl alcohol. Brown prefers to regard it as a steric effect of the bulky t-butoxide ion. He argues that a large base should find it easier to attack the more exposed hydrogens of the methyl groups than those of the ethyl group. Whatever the correct theoretical explanation, the usefulness of the ability to change the orientation by changing the base is obvious.

4.9 THE cis/trans PRODUCT RATIO

Another type of "orientation" effect should be considered briefly. When a 1,2-disubstituted or a more highly substituted olefin is formed, *cis-trans* isomerism may be possible. Thus, 2-bromobutane actually yields *three* products rather than the two indicated previously:

$$CH_3CH_2\overset{\overset{\displaystyle }{}}{\underset{\underset{\displaystyle Br}{|}}{C}}HCH_3 \longrightarrow \underset{H \quad\quad H}{\overset{CH_3 \quad CH_3}{C=C}} + \underset{CH_3 \quad H}{\overset{H \quad\quad CH_3}{C=C}} + CH_3CH_2CH=CH_2$$

The more stable of the isomeric 2-butenes is the *trans* isomer, since the two methyl groups are as far from each other as possible. In the *cis* isomer they are constrained on the same side of the double bond and can interfere with each other. In general, the geometric isomer of an olefin which has the two largest groups *trans* to each other is the more stable.

When the transition state of an E2 reaction possesses double-bond character, it should resemble the olefin geometrically as well. Consequently, the transition state leading to *trans* olefin should be favored over that leading to *cis* olefin. This effect should be the more marked, the greater is the double-bond character of the transition state. These expectations are confirmed by the facts: production of *trans* olefin is generally favored in E2 reactions. The preference, as we would expect, seems to be lower in reactions of onium salts, because of the lesser double-bond character of the transition states.

4.10 SYNTHETIC APPLICATIONS

It is obvious from what we have said so far that anyone wishing to synthesize an olefin has many methods to choose from. The following pages will discuss synthetically-useful elimination reactions, and the considerations that go into the choice of an appropriate method. We will also see that elimination reactions are useful in the degradation of complex organic molecules. The double bond furnishes a point of attack at which the molecule can be chopped into smaller fragments that are easier to identify.

The E2 reactions of alkyl halides are important among methods of olefin synthesis. Here the usual "recipe" involves treating the alkyl halide with a hot solution of potassium hydroxide in ethyl alcohol. The base actually involved in the reaction is probably ethoxide ion, formed in the equilibrium

$$HO^- + C_2H_5OH \rightleftharpoons H_2O + C_2H_5O^-$$

which is shifted to the right by the large excess of ethyl alcohol. A procedure which is becoming increasingly popular is the use of potassium t-butoxide in t-butyl alcohol. As noted above, this enables one to obtain Hofmann-rule orientation from alkyl halides. In addition, higher olefin yields often result because the accompanying displacement reaction (see Chap. 5) is hindered by the bulk of the t-butoxide ion. Finally, the less polar t-butyl alcohol favors the E2 reaction with compounds for which the E1 reaction is difficult to avoid in ethyl alcohol, such as highly-branched tertiary alkyl halides.

Normally, the alkyl halide chosen will be either the bromide or the chloride. Iodides are often too unstable, and fluorides too unreactive, to be useful. For reasons to be discussed in Chap. 5, primary alkyl halides seldom give sufficient yields of olefins to be useful as starting materials. The usual application of the reaction, then, is to secondary and tertiary bromides and chlorides.

Sulfonate esters behave very much like alkyl halides in both E2 and E1 reactions. The ester is formed from the alcohol, so this constitutes an indirect method of dehydrating alcohols. An example is the synthesis of 2-pentene:

$$CH_3CH_2\underset{\underset{\displaystyle OH}{|}}{C}HCH_2CH_3 + C_7H_7SO_2Cl \xrightarrow[(C_5H_5N)]{pyridine} CH_3CH_2\underset{\underset{\displaystyle OSO_2C_7H_7}{|}}{C}HCH_2CH_3$$

$$CH_3CH_2\underset{\underset{\displaystyle OSO_2C_7H_7}{|}}{C}HCH_2CH_3 + C_2H_5O^- \xrightarrow{C_2H_5OH} CH_3CH_2CH=CHCH_3 + C_7H_7SO_3^-$$

Tertiary sulfonate esters are unstable, and the primary esters, like the alkyl halides, give low olefin yields, so the method is usually restricted to secondary esters. Solvolysis of sulfonate esters in solvents such as ethyl alcohol or glacial acetic acid can give olefin by the E1 mechanism, but this method is not as convenient as some other E1 reactions which will be discussed below.

E1 reactions of alkyl halides have already been mentioned and, like the E2 reactions, are normally restricted to secondary and tertiary bromides and chlorides. It is usually preferable, where possible, to use an E2 reaction, as olefin yields are lower in E1 reactions.

The acid-catalyzed dehydration of alcohols follows a mechanism analogous to the E1:

$$\underset{\underset{CH_3}{|}}{\overset{\overset{CH_3}{|}}{CH_3-C-OH}} + H^+ \rightleftharpoons \underset{\underset{CH_3}{|}}{\overset{\overset{CH_3}{|}}{CH_3-C-OH_2^+}}$$

$$\underset{\underset{CH_3}{|}}{\overset{\overset{CH_3}{|}}{CH_3-C-OH_2^+}} \rightleftharpoons \underset{\underset{CH_3}{|}}{\overset{\overset{CH_3}{|}}{CH_3-C^+}} + H_2O$$

$$\underset{\underset{CH_3}{|}}{\overset{\overset{CH_3}{|}}{CH_3-C^+}} \rightleftharpoons CH_2=C\overset{CH_3}{\underset{CH_3}{<}} + H^+$$

In many dehydrations by sulfuric acid a sulfate ester, $ROSO_2OH$, seems to form and then solvolyze to a carbonium ion. Another method of dehydrating alcohols is to pass the hot vapor over a solid catalyst such as alumina (Al_2O_3).

These alcohol dehydrations are often the quickest and simplest procedures for olefin synthesis, but they suffer certain disadvantages. One is that they are usually reversible, and the first-formed products may undergo further reaction. Dehydration of 1-butanol, for example, yields 1-butene which then may react further as follows:

$$CH_3CH_2CH{=}CH_2 + H^+ \rightleftharpoons CH_3CH_2\overset{+}{C}HCH_3$$
$$CH_3CH_2\overset{+}{C}HCH_3 \rightleftharpoons CH_3CH{=}CHCH_3 + H^+$$

Unexpected products may also result from rearrangement, an ever-present possibility in carbonium ion reactions. If the carbonium ion can give a more stable isomeric carbonium ion by a simple 1,2-shift (see Chap. 3), rearrangements are especially likely. This possibility may be illustrated with the carbonium ion from 3-methyl-2-butanol:

$$(CH_3)_2CH\underset{\underset{OH}{|}}{CH}CH_3 \xrightarrow{H^+} (CH_3)_2CH\overset{+}{C}HCH_3$$

$$(CH_3)_2CH\overset{+}{C}HCH_3 \longrightarrow (CH_3)_2C{=}CHCH_3 + (CH_3)_2CHCH{=}CH_2$$

$$\downarrow \text{1,2-shift of H}$$

$$(CH_3)_2\overset{+}{C}CH_2CH_3 \longrightarrow (CH_3)_2C{=}CHCH_3 + CH_2{=}\underset{\underset{}{}}{\overset{\overset{CH_3}{|}}{C}}CH_2CH_3$$

The 2-methyl-1-butene from the rearranged carbonium ion increases the difficulty of isolating a pure product from the reaction. Clearly, E1 reactions should be avoided in such circumstances. Where only a single product is possible or likely, however, as in the dehydration of *t*-butyl alcohol, they will be entirely satisfactory.

The reaction of a tetraalkylammonium ion with base is called the *Hofmann degradation* or *exhaustive methylation*. The meaning of the latter term will become apparent shortly. The procedure can be used either as a method of synthesizing olefins or in the degradation of complex organic compounds.

The starting material can be any primary, secondary or tertiary amine. The amine is treated with an excess of methyl iodide, the resulting tetraalkylammonium iodide converted to the hydroxide, and the hydroxide heated. The sequence of reactions is

$$RCH_2CH_2NH_2 + CH_3I \longrightarrow RCH_2CH_2\overset{+}{N}H_2CH_3 \ I^-$$

$$RCH_2CH_2\overset{+}{N}H_2NHCH_3 \ I^- + NaOH \longrightarrow RCH_2CH_2NHCH_3 + NaI + H_2O$$

$$RCH_2CH_2NHCH_3 \xrightarrow[\text{more NaOH}]{\text{more } CH_3I} RCH_2CH_2\overset{+}{N}(CH_3)_3 \ I^-$$

$$RCH_2CH_2\overset{+}{N}(CH_3)_3 \ I^- + AgOH \longrightarrow RCH_2CH_2\overset{+}{N}(CH_3)_3 \ \overset{-}{O}H + AgI$$

$$RCH_2CH_2\overset{+}{N}(CH_3)_3 \ OH^- \xrightarrow{\text{heat}} RCH=CH_2 + N(CH_3)_3 + H_2O$$

Though the initial methylation occurs in steps, it is usually brought about all at once with an excess of methyl iodide and base. Sometimes the results of this procedure are not very good. In such cases, a tertiary amine may be produced by the Eschweiler-Clarke method:

$$RCH_2CH_2NH_2 + 2HCHO + 2HCOOH \longrightarrow$$
$$RCH_2CH_2N(CH_3)_2 + 2CO_2 + 2H_2O$$

The tertiary amine is then treated with methyl iodide to give the quaternary salt. Another popular modification involves conversion of the iodide to the hydroxide by passage over a basic ion exchange resin, which is more convenient than the use of silver hydroxide. Either method of obtaining the hydroxide gives a relatively dilute aqueous solution. This is concentrated by distillation until olefin begins to come over, and heating is continued until no further product distils.

The applications of this procedure to olefin synthesis are obvious. A more interesting application is in determination of the structures of certain complex naturally-occurring amines. These substances, called *alkaloids,* are found in many plants. Their interesting structures have made them a popular subject for research among organic chemists. We will merely illustrate the application of the Hofmann degradation with some very simple amines.

If the amine is a simple open-chain primary, secondary or tertiary amine, the products of the sequence of reactions outlined above will be a nitrogen-free olefin and a tertiary amine (in our example, trimethylamine). If the amino nitrogen is part of a ring, however, the sequence of steps will be

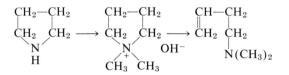

The olefin is not nitrogen free in this case, as the amine function remains attached to the molecule. Removal requires a second application of the Hofmann sequence of reactions:

In this way, one can tell whether the amino function is in an open chain or is part of a ring. The reader can verify for himself that a nitrogen at the juncture of two rings, such as

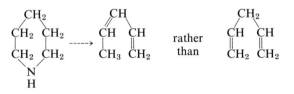

will require *three* applications of the sequence. The reason for the term "exhaustive methylation" should by now be obvious.

Often the double bond is hydrogenated between applications, in the interest of a more stable and easily handled product. When this is not done, double bonds may rearrange into conjugation under the strongly basic conditions:

A final advantage of the method is that the double bond (or bonds) remaining in the nitrogen-free product offers a reactive functional group for further degradation of the molecule. It can, for example, be cleaved by oxidation to give still simpler molecules.

A degradation process very similar to the Hofmann reaction converts a tertiary amine to an *amine oxide* which is then heated:

$$RCH_2CH_2N(CH_3)_2 + H_2O_2 \longrightarrow RCH_2CH_2\overset{\overset{-O}{|}}{\overset{+}{N}}(CH_3)_2 + H_2O$$

$$RCH_2CH_2\overset{\overset{-O}{|}}{\overset{+}{N}}(CH_3)_2 \xrightarrow{\text{heat}} RCH=CH_2 + (CH_3)_2NOH$$

Though this reaction belongs to an entirely different mechanistic class, that of cyclic eliminations, it gives results very similar to those of the Hofmann method and can often be substituted for it; its orientation, however, is not so specific. The less-substituted olefin tends to be favored, but not to any pronounced extent:

$$CH_3CH_2\underset{\overset{|}{\overset{+}{N}}(CH_3)_3\ OH^-}{CHCH_3} \xrightarrow{\text{heat}} CH_3CH_2CH=CH_2 + CH_3CH=CHCH_3$$
$$\phantom{CH_3CH_2CHCH_3 \xrightarrow{\text{heat}}} 95\% 5\%$$

$$CH_3CH_2\underset{\overset{\overset{|}{\overset{+}{N}}(CH_3)_2}{\underset{|}{-O}}}{CHCH_3} \xrightarrow{\text{heat}} CH_3CH_2CH=CH_2 + CH_3CH=CHCH_3$$
$$\phantom{CH_3CH_2CHCH_3 \xrightarrow{\text{heat}}} 67\% 33\%$$

Obviously the preference is much less than in the Hofmann reaction, and barely exceeds the ratio (60:40) of the number of β-hydrogens available for attack in each branch.

Several other pyrolytic *cis* eliminations are of synthetic utility. Esters may be pyrolyzed at 300 to 500°. If the boiling point of the ester is high enough, the reaction may be carried out on the pure liquid. More often, the ester is added at the top of a heated tube packed with glass beads, and the products are swept out into a cooled receiver by a stream of nitrogen.

When the method is employed to prepare simple olefins, the acetate ester is normally used. The reaction is especially efficient for the preparation of 1-alkenes from primary alcohols. Unlike the direct, acid-catalyzed dehydration of alcohols, the reaction conditions do not cause rearrangement of the double bond. When a secondary or tertiary ester is used, the orientation is generally almost random. *sec*-Butyl acetate gives 57% 1-butene and 43% 2-butene, which is close to the 60:40 ratio of the number of hydrogens on the first and third carbon atoms, respectively.

Preparation of olefins is not the only synthetic application of ester pyrolysis. Sometimes it is easier to obtain an acid from an ester by pyrolysis than by hydrolysis, if the ester is highly hindered or contains other functional groups sensitive to hydrolysis. An example is:

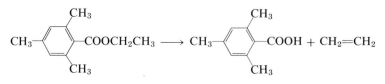

A closely related reaction is the pyrolysis of xanthate esters. The xanthates can be readily prepared from the alcohols, and are often used immediately without purification:

$$2RCH_2CH_2OH + 2Na \longrightarrow 2RCH_2CH_2ONa + H_2$$

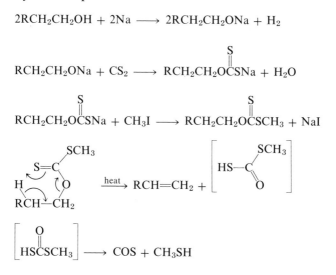

$$\begin{bmatrix} O \\ \| \\ HSCSCH_3 \end{bmatrix} \longrightarrow COS + CH_3SH$$

The mechanism is analogous to that of ordinary ester pyrolysis, though the acid formed is unstable and decomposes to COS and CH_3SH. (These have particularly unpleasant odors, and the reaction must be performed in a hood.)

An advantage over ester pyrolysis is that reaction occurs at a much lower temperature. Usually, heating the liquid xanthate to 100–200° is sufficient. Xanthate ester pyrolysis is therefore preferable to ordinary ester pyrolysis for the preparation of olefins that may decompose at high temperatures. Orientation is nearly random, just as in ester pyrolysis.

No other pyrolytic eliminations are of any general synthetic utility. The pyrolysis of alkyl halides, mentioned earlier, gives results similar to those of the E1 reaction, and usually has no advantage over it.

Elimination of halogen from 1,2-dihalides to give olefins results from treatment with certain active metals (usually zinc), or with iodide ion:

$$\underset{\underset{Br}{|} \quad \underset{Br}{|}}{CH_3CH-CHCH_3} + I^- \longrightarrow CH_3CH=CHCH_3 + IBr + Br^-$$

Usually the 1,2-dihalide is obtained by adding the halogen to an olefin, and the elimination obviously merely completes a synthetically useless circle. Sometimes the addition-elimination sequence is useful as a way of "storing" an unstable olefin: the olefin is converted to the dibromide and regenerated from it when needed.

Another use of 1,2-dihalides is in the preparation of acetylenes via a double E2 reaction:

$$\underset{\substack{|\quad\;\;|\\ Br\;\;\;Br}}{RCH-CHR} \xrightarrow[C_2H_5OH]{KOH} RC{\equiv}CR$$

This method offers a convenient way of converting an olefin to the corresponding acetylene.

CHAPTER 4 REVIEW QUESTIONS

1. Define and give an example of each of the following: E1 mechanism, E2 mechanism, cyclic mechanism, Saytzev rule, Hofmann rule.

2. Explain how the E2 and E1cb mechanisms can be distinguished from one another.

3. Outline the evidence for a *trans* coplanar transition state for the E2 reaction.

4. What is the main objection to acid-catalyzed dehydration of alcohols as a synthetic method of producing olefins?

5. What products would you expect to predominate in the Hofmann reaction of

$$\underset{\underset{CH_3}{|}}{\overset{\overset{CH_3}{|}}{FCH_2CH_2{}^+N{-}CH_2CH_3}} \; OH^-$$

6. What olefin would you expect to obtain from the pyrolysis of

7. What other reactants and reaction conditions would you use if you wished to get a good yield of 1-butene from 2-bromobutane?

5

Substitution vs. Elimination

5.1 GENERAL

We noted earlier that substitution and elimination reactions usually occur simultaneously. We omitted detailed discussion of this fact from Chap. 3 and 4 to avoid undue complication. Since the success or failure of a synthesis will hinge upon the ability of the desired reaction to compete successfully with the side reaction, some understanding of the facts influencing the competition is necessary. There is no point in trying to perform a substitution reaction under circumstances in which elimination to produce olefin will obviously be the predominant path, or vice-versa.

5.2 EFFECT OF STRUCTURE

The effect of the structure of the reactant is perhaps simplest to understand. Starting with the case of competition between the two bimolecular reactions (E2 and S_N2), the prediction is easy. The rate of the S_N2 reaction decreases, and the rate of the E2 reaction increases, with increased chain branching of the reactant. (See Chap. 3 and 4 for the reasons behind these trends.) The olefin yield should therefore increase sharply with increased chain branching. A typical order would be

$$CH_3CH_2X < (CH_3)_2CHX < (CH_3)_3CX$$

In fact, when the alkyl bromides are treated with sodium ethoxide in ethanol, ethyl bromide gives mostly ether, and only 1% of ethylene, while t-butyl bromide gives an almost quantitative yield of isobutylene. Isopropyl bromide gives both propylene and ethyl propyl ether in about a 3:1 ratio.

If the reaction conditions are such that only S_N2 and E2 processes occur, the substitution/elimination ratio remains constant throughout a given reaction, and is unaffected by changes in the concentrations of reactants. It is a general rule that the relative rates of two simultaneous reactions of the same order in the same reactants will be independent of concentration. If the two reactions have rate constants of k_I and k_{II}, then

$$\text{rate}_I = k_I[A][B]$$
$$\text{rate}_{II} = k_{II}[A][B]$$

From which

$$\frac{\text{rate}_I}{\text{rate}_{II}} = \frac{k_I}{k_{II}}$$

Any variation of the substitution/elimination ratio of an E2 reaction with concentration or extent of reaction is thus evidence that a process of different order (S_N1 or E1) is occurring.

The S_N1-E1 reaction occurs in two stages; the substitution/elimination ratio is determined in the second stage:

$$RX \longrightarrow R^+ + X^-$$

$$R^+ \quad \begin{array}{l} \longrightarrow \text{olefin} \\ \longrightarrow \text{substitution product} \end{array}$$

Since the first step is rate-determining and the second step product-determining, there is no necessary relation between the rate and the substitution/elimination ratio. In general, higher yields of substitution products are obtained under S_N1-E1 than under S_N2-E2 conditions. Solvolysis of t-butyl bromide in ethanol, for example, gives 19% of isobutylene and 81% of t-butyl ethyl ether, as opposed to the almost quantitative yield of olefin obtained with ethoxide ion present (S_N2-E2 conditions).

Within the E1-S_N1 category, increased branching of the alkyl group generally leads to increased olefin yield. We learned in Chap. 4 that the more highly substituted olefins are more stable and form more rapidly in both E2 and E1 reactions of halides (Saytzev rule). As the more highly branched carbonium ions will give more highly substituted olefins, the same factor is undoubtedly operating here. t-Amyl bromide, which can give the trisubstituted olefin 2-methyl-2-butene, gives about twice as much olefin as t-butyl bromide, which yields the disubstituted 2-methyl-1-propene:

$$
\begin{array}{c}
\quad\quad CH_3 \\
\quad\quad | \\
CH_3\!-\!\overset{\displaystyle |}{\underset{\displaystyle |}{C}}\!-\!Br \xrightarrow{C_2H_5OH} CH_2\!=\!C(CH_3)_2 + \text{ether} \\
\quad\quad CH_3 \\
\quad\quad\quad\quad\quad\quad\quad 19\% \quad\quad\quad 81\%
\end{array}
$$

$$
\begin{array}{c}
\quad\quad CH_3 \quad\quad\quad\quad\quad\quad\quad\quad\quad\quad\quad\quad CH_3 \\
\quad\quad | \quad\quad\quad\quad\quad\quad\quad\quad\quad\quad\quad\quad\quad\quad | \\
CH_3CH_2\!-\!\overset{\displaystyle |}{\underset{\displaystyle |}{C}}\!-\!Br \xrightarrow{C_2H_5OH} CH_3CH\!=\!C(CH_3)_2 + CH_2CH_2\overset{\displaystyle |}{C}\!=\!CH_2 + \text{ether} \\
\quad\quad CH_3 \\
\quad\quad\quad\quad\quad\quad\quad 30\% \quad\quad\quad\quad\quad 6\% \quad\quad\quad 64\%
\end{array}
$$

Another probable contribution to the increased olefin yield is steric hindrance of the substitution reaction. In a carbonium ion the bond angles are 120°, while in the substitution product they are 109°28′:

$$
\begin{array}{c}
\underset{R\overset{120°}{\wedge}R}{\overset{R}{\underset{}{C^+}}} \quad \xrightarrow{\;C_2H_5OH\;} \quad \underset{R\overset{109°28'}{\underset{R}{\big|}}}{\overset{R}{\underset{}{C}}}\!-\!OC_2H_5
\end{array}
$$

If the alkyl groups are large, they will resist the decrease in bond angle that occurs during substitution, and slow down the substitution process. Bond angles in the olefin, on the other hand, are still 120°, and this steric effect does not operate in olefin formation. The more highly branched the reactant, the more likely this factor becomes. In the simplest cases, such as t-butyl vs. t-amyl halides, the increased ease of olefin formation mentioned earlier is probably the only important effect.

5.3 EFFECT OF THE LEAVING GROUP

Another structural feature that influences the course of elimination reactions is the nature of the leaving group X. We noted above that the action of ethoxide ion on ethyl bromide gave only 1% of ethylene, the major product being diethyl ether from an S_N2 process. With ethyldimethylsulfonium ion $(X = \overset{+}{S}(CH_3)_2)$ the ethylene yield is 20%. With ethyltrimethylammonium ion $(X = \overset{+}{N}(CH_3)_3)$, the ethylene yield rises to 70%. Even here it is often not easy to make elimination predominate, as other primary alkyltrimethylammonium ions give about 10–20% olefin under the same conditions, because alkyl substitution cuts down the rate of elimination from these compounds according to the Hofmann rule (see Chap. 4). A way of increasing the olefin yield from alkyltrimethylammonium salts will be mentioned when we discuss the effect of solvent.

The leaving group should have no effect on olefin yield in E1 reactions, for the relative reactivity of the carbonium ion toward substitution and elimination should be the same, no matter what the leaving group was. For example, the same t-butyl carbonium ion should arise from t-butyl chloride, t-butyl bromide, or t-butyldimethylsulfonium ion. In most cases, this prediction is true. Recently, however, Winstein has discovered some cases where the olefin yield *does* depend on the leaving group in E1 reactions, being greater for halides than for sulfonium salts. The effect was especially marked in acetic acid. Since this solvent is not very good at solvating free ions, elimination was probably occurring from *ion pairs* (R^+X^-), in which the leaving group is still close to the carbonium ion.

5.4 EFFECT OF SOLVENT AND BASE

A change in reaction conditions can also affect the olefin yield. Though we will discuss separately the effects of solvent and base on E2-S_N2 reactions, it is not always possible in practice to decide which predominates. The base is usually the so-called *conjugate base* of the solvent, derived through loss of a proton from a solvent molecule. Examples are hydroxide ion from water and ethoxide ion from ethanol. In such cases, a change of solvent necessarily entails a change of base. If we try to bypass this problem by comparing potassium hydroxide in water with potassium hydroxide in ethanol, we are frustrated by the rapidly established equilibrium

$$HO^- + C_2H_5OH \rightleftharpoons H_2O + C_2H_5O^-$$

Because ethanol is present in large excess, the equilibrium lies toward the right. The added hydroxide becomes ethoxide whether we want it to or not.

When discussing the effect of structure of the base, we must consider two properties of a base which may not vary similarly with structure. These are the *basicity,* or affinity for protons, and the *nucleophilicity,* or the ability to form bonds to carbon atoms. The former is easily measured for a base, B, by determining the equilibrium constant for

$$B + H_3O^+ \rightleftharpoons BH^+ + H_2O$$

The latter can be measured by determining the reactivity of B in some typical S_N2 reaction, such as that with methyl bromide.

A representative set of nucleophilicities run in the order

$$H_2O < CH_3CO_2^- < Cl^- < OH^- < I^- < SH^-$$

A number of discrepancies between this order and the order of basicities are apparent. The basicities (in water) run as follows:

$$H_2O \sim I^- \sim Cl^- < CH_3CO_2^- < SH^- < OH^-$$

Though hydroxide ion is by far the most basic of the group, both I^- and SH^- are better nucleophiles. Again, acetate ion is a stronger base than iodide or chloride. Though the order of nucleophilicity may vary with the reaction or the conditions used to measure it, there remain differences of the sort just mentioned.

The effect of the solvent on the $S_N2/E2$ ratio depends on how well it solvates the two transition states, for the reactants are the same for both reactions. Let us consider attack by hydroxide ion on ethyl bromide. The charge is concentrated on the oxygen atom in the reactant. In the S_N2 transition state, it is spread over *three* atoms:

$$\underbrace{HO\text{---}\overset{\overset{\displaystyle CH_3}{|}}{CH_2}\text{---}Br}$$

In the E2 transition state, it is spread over *five* atoms:

$$HO\text{---}H\text{---}CH_2\text{==}CH_2\text{---}X$$

Charge is dispersed in both reactions, so both will be favored by less polar solvents. This arises because a polar solvent increases activation energy by stabilizing the concentrated charge of the hydroxide ion more efficiently than the dispersed charge of the transition state. This effect is more pronounced in the E2 reaction, where the extent of charge dispersal is greater. A less polar solvent, then, favors the E2 more than the S_N2 reaction. By analogous reasoning, attack of an anionic base on a sulfonium or ammonium salt should give higher elimination/substitution ratios in less polar solvents. This reasoning is another application of the Hughes-Ingold theory of solvation, which we first saw applied to substitution reactions alone in Chap. 3.

These predictions of the effects of solvent and base are in general accord with experimental results. Olefin yields are usually better in ethanol-ethoxide than in water-hydroxide mixtures. In recent years, *t*-butoxide ion in *t*-butyl alcohol has been used in elimination reactions, and appears to be still better than ethoxide ion in ethanol. This is as expected, for *t*-butyl alcohol is a less polar solvent than ethanol, and *t*-butoxide is a stronger base than ethoxide.

In apparent contradiction of these generalizations, pyrolyses of tetra-alkylammonium hydroxides give better olefin yields than do reactions of the corresponding salts with either ethanol-ethoxide or *t*-butyl alcohol-*t*-butoxide mixtures. For example, *n*-butyltrimethylammonium hydroxide gives 75–80% olefin on pyrolysis, while olefin constitutes only one-third of the product when the same ammonium ion is treated with *t*-butyl alcohol-*t*-butoxide, and only $\frac{1}{10}$ when treated with ethanol-ethoxide. There is evidently something unusual about the pyrolysis. It is performed by distilling a solution of the hydroxide until olefin comes over. By this time the solution is usually a thick syrup, much more concentrated than is normal for solution reactions. Possibly so much water has been removed that the hydroxide ion is less solvated and thus more reactive (i.e., more basic) than in dilute solution.

5.5 EFFECT OF TEMPERATURE

A final factor to consider is temperature. Usually, two competing reactions have different activation energies. The larger the activation energy, the slower the reaction at any given temperature, but the faster the increase in rate with increase in temperature. Thus, a process of high activation energy that contributes little to the overall reaction at room temperature may become predominant at 100°. Suppose, for example, that reaction A is five times faster than reaction B, but the rate of A only doubles with a ten-degree rise in temperature, while the rate of B triples. By the time the temperature has risen forty degrees, B is as fast as A (a change from 5:1 to 80:81 in relative rates). Beyond a forty-degree increase, B becomes the predominant reaction. It happens that elimination reactions usually have higher activation energies than the accompanying substitution reactions, so increasing the temperature increases the elimination /substitution ratio.

CHAPTER 5 REVIEW QUESTIONS

1. Define, and distinguish between, basicity and nucleophilicity.

2. What is the effect of steric hindrance in the E1 reaction? In the E2 reaction?

3. Why is elimination favored over substitution by an increase in temperature?

4. How would you prepare ethyl isopropyl ether if you wished to minimize olefin formation?

5. What type of reactant generally gives the best olefin yield in an E2 reaction?

6. Which should give more olefin in solvolysis, t-butyl chloride or tri-isopropyl-carbinyl chloride?

7. Predict the effect of changing from water to 50% dioxane-50% water on the rates of the following reactions:

(a) $(CH_3)_3CCl + H_2O \longrightarrow (CH_3)_3COH + (CH_3)_2C{=}CH_2 + HCl$

(b) $(CH_3)_2CHS(CH_3)_2^+ + OH^- \longrightarrow$
$$CH_2{=}CHCH_3 + S(CH_3)_2 + H_2O$$

(c) $C_2H_5Br + SH^- \longrightarrow C_2H_5SH + Br^-$

6
Effect of Unsaturated Substituents and of Conjugation

6.1 ADDITIONS TO CONJUGATED OLEFINS

Treatment of a conjugated diene with a halogen results in the expected *1,2-addition* across one of the double bonds, but also gives some *1,4-addition* to the ends of the conjugated system:

$$CH_2{=}CH{-}CH{=}CH_2 + X_2 \longrightarrow$$

$$CH_2{=}CH{-}\underset{X}{\underset{|}{CH}}{-}\underset{X}{\underset{|}{CH_2}} + \underset{X}{\underset{|}{CH_2}}{-}CH{=}CH{-}\underset{X}{\underset{|}{CH_2}}$$

The remaining double bond in the 1,4-adduct is shifted into the middle of the molecule. Under most conditions the 1,2-adduct is formed in larger amount, though always accompanied by 1,4-adduct. Many textbooks report that bromine addition to 1,3-butadiene gives 80% of the 1,4-adduct and 20% of the 1,2-adduct. In fact, this is the *equilibrium* mixture (thermodynamic control) of the two isomers, for they are easily interconverted under all but the mildest reaction conditions. The 1,2-isomer is almost always formed in greater yield under conditions of *kinetic control* (see Chap. 1 for definitions of these terms).

The addition of halogens to dienes is undoubtedly a stepwise process, just as it is with simple olefins. The intermediate could be either a halonium ion or a carbonium ion:

$$\overset{X}{\underset{+}{\triangle}}\; CH_2{-}CH{-}CH{=}CH_2 \quad or \quad \overset{X}{\underset{|}{C}}H_2{-}\overset{+}{C}H{-}CH{=}CH_2$$

The halonium ion can react with halide to give a 1,2-adduct in the same manner as a simple olefin:

$$\overset{X}{\underset{+}{\triangle}}\; CH_2{-}CH{-}CH{=}CH_2 + X^- \longrightarrow \overset{X}{\underset{|}{C}}H_2{-}\underset{X}{\underset{|}{CH}}{-}CH{=}CH_2$$

The carbonium ion, however, has a vacant p orbital next to the π orbital of the double bond, and these orbitals can overlap to give a π orbital spread over three atoms:

In resonance terminology, the carbonium ion can be depicted as a hybrid of the two structures:

$$\overset{X}{\underset{|}{C}}H_2-\overset{+}{C}H-CH=CH_2 \longleftrightarrow \overset{X}{\underset{|}{C}}H_2-CH=CH-\overset{+}{C}H_2$$

The positive charge is divided between the second and fourth carbon atoms. We can thus expect a halide ion to react with either of these two positions and give either the 1,2-adduct or the 1,4-adduct:

$$\overset{X}{\underset{|}{C}}H_2-\overset{+\frac{1}{2}}{C}H\text{=\hspace{-3pt}=}CH\text{=\hspace{-3pt}=}\overset{+\frac{1}{2}}{C}H_2 + X^- \longrightarrow \begin{cases} \overset{X}{\underset{|}{C}}H_2-\overset{X}{\underset{|}{C}}H-CH=CH_2 \\ \quad\text{and} \\ \overset{X}{\underset{|}{C}}H_2-CH=CH-\overset{X}{\underset{|}{C}}H_2 \end{cases}$$

The presence of the resonance hybrid carbonium ion explains all the facts, though it is possible that all or part of the 1,2-adduct is formed from a halonium ion. Another possibility is that the actual intermediate is a resonance hybrid of the two carbonium-ion *and* the halonium-ion structures.

Other reactions that have carbonium-ion intermediates, such as addition of HX, also give mixtures of products:

$$CH_2{=}CH-CH{=}CH_2 + HCl \longrightarrow \begin{cases} CH_3-\overset{Cl}{\underset{|}{C}}H-CH=CH_2 \quad\text{(1,2)} \\ \quad\text{and} \\ CH_3-CH=CH-\overset{Cl}{\underset{|}{C}}H_2 \quad\text{(1,4)} \end{cases}$$

Here again, the 1,4-adduct predominates at equilibrium, but more 1,2-adduct is formed under conditions of kinetic control. The products of HBr addition equilibrate so rapidly that it is difficult to avoid a predominance of 1,4-adduct.

The ability of the double bond in the intermediate to "spread out" the positive charge generally results in increased reactivity. The resonance stabilization of the intermediate is found also in the transition state leading to it, and hence the activation energy is lower for addition to diene than for addition to a comparable simple olefin.

This reasoning applies whether or not 1,4-addition actually occurs. When a benzene ring is attached to the double bond, as in $C_6H_5CH=CH_2$, the intermediate is resonance stabilized as follows:

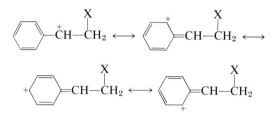

The product is exclusively the 1,2-addend:

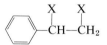

Reaction of halide ion at one of the ring positions bearing positive charge would have given a product without the high stability of the cyclic conjugated system of benzene. Evidence that the stabilization of the intermediate pictured above is real is found in the much higher reactivity of $C_6H_5CH=CH_2$ than of $RCH=CH_2$.

A benzene ring attached to the double bond determines orientation in addition of unsymmetrical addends:

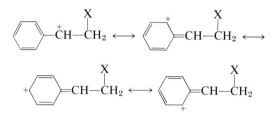

Usually the orienting effect of the benzene ring overrides that of an alkyl group:

In general, a substituent that can stabilize the positive charge of the intermediate by resonance directs addition of the anionic part of the addend adjacent to the substituent itself. We have already seen a simple example of this rule in Chap. 2, where addition to a halogen-substituted double bond was discussed.

6.2 RESONANCE-STABILIZED CARBONIUM IONS: ALLYLIC REARRANGEMENTS

The stabilizing effect of an unsaturated substituent on a carbonium ion should not depend on the manner in which the ion is produced. We have seen in Chap. 3 that S_N1 reactions involve carbonium-ion intermediates. Thus, unsaturated substituents should facilitate these reactions too.

The facts bear out this reasoning very well. Normally, primary halides are extremely reluctant to react by the S_N1 mechanism, preferring the S_N2 mechanism where possible. Allyl chloride and benzyl chloride,

$$CH_2=CHCH_2Cl \quad \text{and} \quad \text{[benzene ring]}—CH_2Cl$$

are far more reactive than normal primary halides in S_N1 reactions. In fact, their reactivity approaches that of tertiary halides. Resonance stabilization of the carbonium ions has again made their formation much easier:

$$CH_2=CH-CH_2^+ \longleftrightarrow {}^+CH_2-CH=CH_2$$

$$\text{[ring]}—CH_2^+ \longleftrightarrow \text{[ring]}=CH_2 \longleftrightarrow {}^+\text{[ring]}=CH_2 \longleftrightarrow \text{[ring]}=CH_2$$

Substitution of additional phenyl groups on the carbon atom that will bear the positive charge increases reactivity still more. Rates of S_N1 reactions increase sharply in the following order:

$$C_6H_5CH_2Cl < (C_6H_5)CHCl < (C_6H_5)_3CCl$$

| benzyl chloride | benzhydryl chloride | triphenylmethyl chloride |

This sequence arises from increasing resonance stabilization of the carbonium ion. Benzyl carbonium ion can spread the charge over four positions (CH_2 group + 3 ring positions), while benzhydryl can spread it over seven (CH group + 3 positions in each of two rings), and triphenylmethyl can spread it over ten (C atom + 3 positions in each of 3 rings).

Triphenylmethyl carbonium ion is so highly stabilized that, unlike most carbonium ions, it can be stored over appreciable periods of time. In an ionizing but non-nucleophilic solvent such as liquid sulfur dioxide, covalent triphenylmethyl chloride is in equilibrium with the ionized form:

$$(C_6H_5)_3CCl \overset{SO_2}{\rightleftharpoons} (C_6H_5)_3C^+ + Cl^-$$

Salts of triphenylmethyl carbonium ion with non-nucleophilic anions such as perchlorate can be made, provided that atmospheric moisture is rigorously excluded. Triphenylcarbinol ionizes in concentrated sulfuric acid according to the equation:

$$(C_6H_5)_3COH + 2H_2SO_4 \longrightarrow (C_6H_5)_3C^+ + H_3O^+ + 2HSO_4^-$$

In S_N1 reactions of benzyl halides, the incoming group always becomes attached to the carbon atom that bore the leaving group, since attachment at a ring position would give a product without the resonance stabilization of the benzene ring. With allylic halides this restriction does not apply, and rearranged products are obtained:

$$CH_3CH=CHCH_2Cl \xrightarrow{H_2O/acetone} \begin{cases} CH_3CH=CHCH_2OH \\ \quad \text{and} \\ CH_3CH-CH=CH_2 \\ \quad\ \ OH \end{cases}$$

The two products correspond to reaction of water with the carbonium ion,

$$CH_3\overset{+\frac{1}{2}}{CH}=CH=\overset{+\frac{1}{2}}{CH_2}$$

at the first and third carbon atoms, respectively. We find that the isomeric chloride

$$CH_3CH-CH=CH_2 \\ \quad\ \ Cl$$

which should give the same carbonium ion, also gives a mixture of the two alcohols. The mixtures from the two chlorides are not quite identical in composition, apparently because a little of the product in each case arises from S_N2 displacement by solvent without rearrangement. Allylic rearrangements are quite general in carbonium-ion reactions of allylic compounds. In syntheses of single, pure isomers of such compounds, we must therefore avoid any reactions having carbonium-ion intermediates.

A particularly interesting aspect of allylic rearrangements is the tendency for conversion of one isomer to another to occur without any other evidence of reaction. Under a good many circumstances, such as heat or the presence of catalysts (acids or certain metal salts), a pure allylic halide may be partly or entirely changed into its allylic isomer. In many instances this undoubtedly involves formation of the carbonium ion, which then reacts with the halide ion to give product mixtures:

$$CH_3CH=CHCH_2Br \longrightarrow CH_3\overset{+\frac{1}{2}}{CH}=CH=\overset{+\frac{1}{2}}{CH_2} \xrightarrow{Br^-} \begin{cases} CH_3CH=CHCH_2Br \\ \quad \text{and} \\ CH_3CHCH=CH_2 \\ \quad\ \ Br \end{cases}$$

In certain cases, such rearrangement occurs when free carbonium ions do not seem to be involved. For example, solvolysis of α,α-dimethylallyl chloride in acetic acid gives both solvolysis products and rearranged chloride:

$$CH_2=CH-\underset{\underset{CH_3}{|}}{\overset{\overset{CH_3}{|}}{C}}-Cl \xrightarrow{CH_3COOH} CH_2=CH-\underset{\underset{CH_3}{|}}{\overset{\overset{CH_3}{|}}{C}}-O\overset{O}{\overset{\|}{C}}CH_3$$

$$+ CH_3\overset{O}{\overset{\|}{C}}O-CH_2-CH=C\overset{CH_3}{\underset{CH_3}{<}} \quad + Cl-CH_2-CH=C\overset{CH_3}{\underset{CH_3}{<}}$$

The rearranged chloride could not have come from reaction with free chloride ion in solution. Reaction mixtures containing added radioactive chloride ion give rearranged chloride containing very little of the radioactivity, while a free carbonium ion would pick up active and inactive chloride ion indiscriminately.

For such reasons, the isomerization is believed to be a case of *internal return* from an ion-pair† intermediate:

$$\underset{Cl^-}{\underline{\overset{+\frac{1}{2}}{CH_2}{=\!=}CH{=\!=}\overset{+\frac{1}{2}}{C}(CH_3)_2}}$$

The carbonium ion and the chloride ion are never free of each other, and can react to form either covalent isomer. Evidence for internal return has been found in many solvolyses in relatively poor ion-solvating solvents (especially acetic acid) of reactants that can form moderately stable carbonium ions.

6.3 PHENYL PARTICIPATION AND PHENONIUM IONS

The ability of a phenyl group to facilitate S_N1 reactions often persists even when it is not a substituent on the same carbon atom as the leaving group. For example, 2-phenylethyl p-toluenesulfonate solvolyzes more rapidly than expected in formic acid. Furthermore, if we label one carbon atom of the ethyl group with radioactive carbon, we find the label distributed between the two positions in the product:

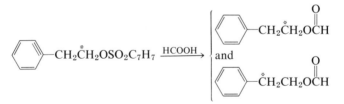

The "scrambling" of the label can be accounted for by an intermediate in which the two positions are equivalent:

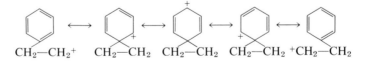

This intermediate can react with formic acid at either of the two CH_2 groups to give the two isotopic "isomers" obtained. This cumbersome pic-

† See Sec. 3.3.

ture of all the contributors to the resonance hybrid is often replaced by a
single structure with dashed lines:

Such a structure is called a *phenonium ion*. Though it is not shown in per-
spective here, the benzene ring must occupy a plane perpendicular to the
plane of the paper, since the atom by which it is attached to the CH_2 groups
is essentially sp^3 hybridized.

If a phenonium ion is being formed while the *p*-toluenesulfonate is
leaving, then the rate enhancement can be explained by saying that the
phenyl group assists the ionization. The π electrons of the benzene ring
can be regarded as displacing the leaving group.

Another consequence of a phenonium-ion intermediate is found in the
stereochemistry of the reaction. There are, of course, no asymmetric carbon atoms in 2-phenylethyl *p*-toluenesulfonate, but there are two in
3-phenyl-2-butyl *p*-toluenesulfonate. It thus has four (2^2) possible optical
isomers, or two ($\pm$) pairs that are diastereomers of each other. These are
called *threo* and *erythro* diastereomers. It was found that solvolysis of *threo*
isomer gives only *threo* product, and of *erythro* isomer only *erythro* product. For example:

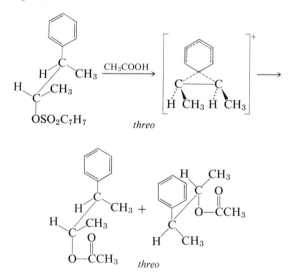

A little mental manipulation of these pictures will show that the products
are enantiomers; i.e., members of the *same* ($\pm$) pair, called the *threo*
isomer. If the intermediate had been a simple "classical" carbonium ion,
the products would have been diastereomers:

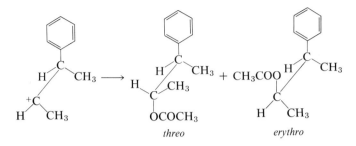

threo   *erythro*

This stereochemical criterion for the phenonium ion is the best evidence in its favor. The rate of ionization is not dramatically increased in many instances (the effect is very small with 3-phenyl-2-butyl *p*-toluenesulfonate) because the phenyl group exerts an unfavorable electron-attracting effect on the ionization. Unless the extent of participation is large, this effect can partly or wholly counterbalance the assistance to ionization. The extent of rate enhancement is often difficult to judge, because there are no generally accepted rules for determining what the rate would be if there were no participation. Finally, the "scrambling" of the label in 2-phenylethyl *p*-toluenesulfonate is not conclusive, since it could also result from rearrangement—by simple 1,2-shifts of the phenyl group from one CH_2 group to the other, without any phenonium ion:

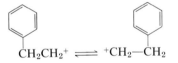

$$CH_2CH_2^+ \rightleftharpoons {}^+CH_2—CH_2$$

6.4 EFFECTS OF NEIGHBORING GROUPS

Participation by a phenyl group to give a phenonium ion is a specific example of the wider field of *neighboring group effects*. Much of our knowledge of this area comes from the extensive investigations of S. Winstein.†
Any group possessing π electrons or an unshared electron pair is, in principle, capable of aiding ionization in S_N1 reactions if it is in a suitable position for participation. Reactions accompanied by neighboring group participation can be depicted generally as:

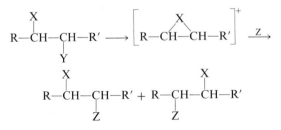

† For a biographical sketch, see footnote, p. 35.

Here Y is the leaving group, X the neighboring group, and Z a nucleophile. Rate enhancement and control of stereochemistry are shown by many neighboring groups other than phenyl. Note also that the two products in our general example will be structurally different if R and R' are not identical, so participation can lead to rearrangement as well.

Halogens are prominent among examples of neighboring groups. We saw in Chap. 2 that halonium ions can be intermediates in addition of halogens to double bonds. They can also be formed if an S_N1 reaction is carried out on a carbon atom adjacent to one bearing a halogen. Evidence that this occurs is found in the solvolysis in acetic acid of *trans*-2-iodocyclohexyl *p*-toluenesulfonate:

This substance solvolyzes over one thousand times faster than cyclohexyl *p*-toluenesulfonate itself, undoubtedly forming the ion:

Iodine is electron-withdrawing relative to hydrogen, so a simple inductive effect without participation would have slowed down the solvolysis rather than accelerated it.

Stereochemistry provides additional evidence for halogen participation. Both isomers of 2-bromocyclohexanol give *trans*-1,2-dibromocyclohexane on treatment with hydrogen bromide:

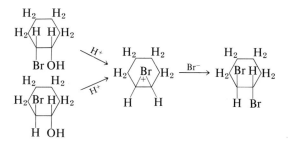

These reactions illustrate another point: the bridged ion can be formed *after* (as well as during) ionization. Obviously the bromine in the *cis* reactant cannot aid the displacement of the leaving group ($-OH_2^+$), for it is on the wrong side of the ring.

Sulfides and amines make especially effective neighboring groups. For example, β,β-dichlorodiethyl sulfide (better known as mustard gas) hydrolyzes much more rapidly than expected, undoubtedly with participation of sulfur:

$$ClCH_2CH_2SCH_2CH_2Cl \rightleftharpoons$$

$$ClCH_2CH_2\overset{+}{S}\overset{CH_2}{\underset{CH_2}{\diagdown|}} + Cl^- \xrightarrow{H_2O} ClCH_2CH_2SCH_2CH_2OH$$

The second chlorine can be hydrolyzed in an analogous manner. A similar case of participation by nitrogen illustrates the occurrence of rearrangement:

$$(C_2H_5)_2NCH_2\underset{\underset{Cl}{|}}{C}HC_2H_5 \longrightarrow$$

$$(C_2H_5)_2\overset{+}{N}\overset{}{\underset{CH_2}{\diagdown}}\!-\!CHC_2H_5 \xrightarrow{OH^-} (C_2H_5)_2N\!-\!\underset{\underset{CH_2OH}{|}}{C}HC_2H_5$$

(The hydroxide ion attacks preferentially at the primary carbon atom of the intermediate.)

We saw another example of neighboring group effects in Chap. 3; the formation of epoxides from halohydrins:

$$HOCH_2CH_2Cl + OH^- \rightleftharpoons {}^-OCH_2CH_2Cl$$

$$\underset{CH_2CH_2Cl}{\overset{O^-}{\diagdown}\!|} \longrightarrow \underset{CH_2\!-\!CH_2}{\overset{O}{\diagup\diagdown}} + Cl^-$$

Here the anionic oxygen of the intermediate is the neighboring group.

Aside from their interest for purposes of theory, neighboring group effects are also of practical concern to the synthetic organic chemist. Their use in obtaining a product of definite stereochemistry is obvious. It is also important to know when participation to give a rearranged product is likely, so that rearrangement can be avoided or encouraged as desired.

6.5 EFFECTS OF PHENYL GROUPS ON ELIMINATION REACTIONS

Phenyl groups exert a very pronounced effect on elimination reactions. We noted earlier that ethyl bromide reacts with sodium ethoxide to give mainly diethyl ether (the S_N2 product) and only a trace of ethylene (the E2 product). In contrast, 2-phenylethyl bromide reacts much faster and yields almost entirely olefin:

$$C_6H_5CH_2CH_2Br + C_2H_5O^- \longrightarrow C_6H_5CH=CH_2$$

The E2 reaction is also accelerated by an α-phenyl group (as in 1-phenylethyl bromide), though not so much as it is by a β-phenyl group.

One reason for the effect of a phenyl group is that conjugation of the double bond with the phenyl group increases the stability of both. The π electrons of the benzene ring and of the double bond can spread out over the whole system, and this new π orbital is of lower energy than the orbitals that coalesced to form it. This effect can obviously operate just as well with an α-phenyl as with a β-phenyl substituent.

The reason that a β-phenyl substituent is in practice more effective is probably as follows. We saw in Chap. 4 that some E2 reactions seem to have transition states with some carbanion character at the β-carbon. If we consider the hypothetical case in which the β-proton is completely removed before the leaving group has begun to depart, we would find a full negative charge on the β-carbon. This charge can be distributed around the benzene ring by resonance:

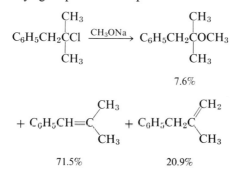

This extreme picture of the transition state seems to be correct for very few E2 reactions, but in many cases the C—H bond appears to be more nearly broken than the C—X bond in the transition state. The partial negative charge on the β-carbon can be stabilized by the phenyl group in the same manner as the full negative charge above. In agreement with this idea, it is to be observed that electron-withdrawing substituents on the benzene ring accelerate, and electron-repelling substituents hinder, E2 reactions of 2-phenylethyl derivatives. A typical order of reactivity is:

$$Cl\text{—}\langle\text{ring}\rangle\text{—}CH_2CH_2Br > \langle\text{ring}\rangle\text{—}CH_2CH_2Br > CH_3\text{—}\langle\text{ring}\rangle\text{—}CH_2CH_2Br$$

The accelerating effect of phenyl makes it evident that elimination toward a β-carbon bearing a phenyl group will be favored over elimination into a plain alkyl group. For example:

$$C_6H_5CH_2\underset{\underset{CH_3}{|}}{\overset{\overset{CH_3}{|}}{C}}Cl \xrightarrow{CH_3ONa} C_6H_5CH_2\underset{\underset{CH_3}{|}}{\overset{\overset{CH_3}{|}}{C}}OCH_3$$

7.6%

$$+ \; C_6H_5CH{=}C\overset{\diagup CH_3}{\diagdown CH_3} \quad + \; C_6H_5CH_2C\overset{\diagup CH_2}{\diagdown CH_3}$$

71.5%   20.9%

The predominant product is the conjugated olefin, even though elimination into one of the methyl groups would be favored by probability (2 methyl groups to one $C_6H_5CH_2$ group). Elimination toward the phenyl group is favored, regardless of whether the reactant is of a type normally obeying the Hofmann rule or the Saytzev rule, since the phenyl group can stabilize either a partial negative charge on the β-carbon or a developing double bond.

6.6 HYPERCONJUGATION

Finally, we will discuss briefly a phenomenon called *hyperconjugation*. In Chap. 4, we noted that alkyl substitution on the double bond increases the stability of an olefin. For example, the stabilities of some simple olefins are in the order:

$$CH_2{=}CH_2 < CH_3CH{=}CH_2 < CH_3CH{=}CHCH_3$$

It has been suggested that this beneficial effect of alkyl substitution arises from overlap of the C—H bonding electrons of the alkyl group with the π electrons of the double bond:

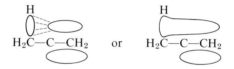

In terms of resonance, hyperconjugation is pictured as follows:

$$\overset{\text{H}}{\underset{|}{\text{H}_2\text{C}}}{-}\text{CH}{=}\text{CH}_2 \longleftrightarrow \text{H}_2\text{C}{=}\text{CH}{-}\overset{\text{H}^+}{\overset{}{\text{C}}}\overset{-}{\text{H}}_2$$

There has been much controversy over the importance of hyperconjugation as a factor in olefin stability. Many now believe that it makes little, if any, contribution. The difficulty arises from a lack of experimental evidence consistent only with hyperconjugation. The situation is too complex and uncertain to describe in the space available here. Whatever the correct theoretical explanation, the fact remains that alkyl substitution promotes olefin stability.

An area where the evidence for hyperconjugation is better is that of carbonium-ion reactions. As noted in Chap. 2 and 3, alkyl substitution greatly increases the stability of carbonium ions. Part of this influence lies in the electron-repelling inductive effect of alkyl groups, but part is probably also a result of hyperconjugation:

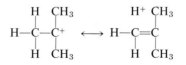

Evidence that there is interaction of the C—H bonds with the carbonium-ion center is found when deuterium is substituted for hydrogen. The formation of the carbonium ion (from alkyl chloride, for example) is slowed down as much as 10–20% per deuterium atom. If the carbon-deuterium bond were not being weakened in the ionization, the effect of deuterium would be negligible.

CHAPTER 6 REVIEW QUESTIONS

1. Define the following terms: neighboring group effect, hyperconjugation, internal return.

2. Arrange in order of increasing S_N1 reactivity: 1-phenyl-1-propyl chloride, 2-phenyl-1-propyl chloride, 3-phenyl-1-propyl chloride.

3. Would you expect optically active or inactive product in the acetolysis of *erythro*-3-phenyl-2-butyl *p*-toluenesulfonate? Explain.

4. Which of the following reactions of crotyl alcohol would you expect to give unrearranged product?
  (a) Reaction with concentrated hydrochloric acid.
  (b) Reaction with sodium metal.
  (c) Esterification with acetic anhydride.
  (d) Reaction with phosphorus tribromide.

5. Why does solvolysis of benzyl bromide never give any products of allylic rearrangement?

6. Predict the products obtained when each of the following isomers is treated with sodium ethoxide in ethanol:

7

Organometallic Compounds and Electrophilic Aliphatic Substitution

7.1 DEFINITION OF ELECTROPHILIC SUBSTITUTION

In addition to nucleophilic substitution reactions (discussed in Chap. 3) there are also electrophilic substitution reactions. They differ from the former in the manner in which bond-breaking and bond-making occur. In an electrophilic substitution, the leaving group departs *without* the electron pair that bound it to the carbon, and the incoming group is electron-deficient rather than electron-rich. Many examples of this type of reaction are found in the formation and reactions of organometallic compounds (substances having a carbon-metal bond).

7.2 MECHANISMS

Before we look at specific examples, we should consider briefly the possible mechanisms of electrophilic reactions. By analogy to S_N (substitution, nucleophilic), these are called S_E (substitution, electrophilic). Again, there are two main possibilities. In the one-stage, bimolecular (S_E2) process, the departure of the leaving group and attack by the incoming group are synchronous:

$$Y^+ + R:X \longrightarrow R:Y + X^+$$

The other possibility (S_E1) is a two-stage process in which the first stage is a unimolecular decomposition of RX:

$$R:X \longrightarrow R:^- + X^+$$
$$R:^- + Y^+ \longrightarrow R:Y$$

Other mechanisms have been suggested, but nearly all of them are just

96

elaborations of the S_E1 or S_E2 processes. Less progress has been made in studying mechanisms of electrophilic than of nucleophilic substitutions, as there are far fewer electrophilic reactions amenable to simple kinetic study.

7.3 ORGANOMETALLIC COMPOUNDS

Organometallic compounds are most often prepared by reaction of an alkyl halide with the appropriate metal. Two examples are:

$$RX + 2Li \longrightarrow RLi + LiX$$

$$RX + Mg \longrightarrow RMgX$$

These examples are not random choices; they are, rather, the usual methods of preparing the two most important organometallic compounds in synthetic organic chemistry.

The second, in particular, is very widely used in organic synthesis. It is called the *Grignard reagent* after Victor Grignard.† Grignard reagents can be formed very simply, by adding a solution of alkyl halide in dry ether to clean, dry magnesium turnings. Almost any alkyl halide will form a Grignard reagent, the only large class of exceptions being alkyl fluorides. For the other halides, the reactivity runs $RI > RBr > RCl$; but even the chlorides can usually be made to react. More will be said later about the structure and reactions of Grignard reagents.

Many organometallic compounds can be made in reactions that start with other organometallic compounds. In fact, this is often the only procedure that will work for preparing compounds of the less active metals. Reaction of an organometallic compound with a metal halide is usually used in such instances:

$$C_6H_5MgBr + AgBr \longrightarrow C_6H_5Ag + MgBr_2$$

$$2CH_3MgCl + CdCl_2 \longrightarrow (CH_3)_2Cd + 2MgCl_2$$

$$CH_3MgCl + HgCl_2 \longrightarrow CH_3HgCl + MgCl_2$$

Note that this procedure uses a salt of a metal lower in the electromotive series than the metal of the organometallic reactant. To convert an organometallic compound to one having a more active metal, reaction with the metal itself is used:

$$(CH_3)_2Hg + 2Na \longrightarrow CH_3Na + Na(Hg)$$

Other reactions that convert one organometallic compound into another include halogen-metal interchange:

$$C_6H_5Br + C_4H_9Li \longrightarrow C_6H_5Li + C_4H_9Br$$

† V. Grignard, 1871–1935. French. Received the Nobel Prize in 1912 for his extensive work on the reactions of organomagnesium halides.

This reaction exchanges the organic group attached to the metal rather than the metal itself. The same is true of the process called *metalation:*

$$C_6H_6 + C_2H_5Na \longrightarrow C_6H_5Na + C_2H_6$$

Since RNa has much ionic character, it is best represented by

$$R^-Na^+$$

and the above reaction therefore means that $C_2H_5^-$ has more affinity for a proton than does $C_6H_5^-$. We may put it another way: C_6H_6 is a stronger acid than C_2H_6. Another reaction of the same type is:

$$C_6H_5CH_3 + C_6H_5Na \longrightarrow C_6H_5CH_2Na + C_6H_6$$

We now can rank the acidities of the hydrocarbons in the order

$$C_6H_5CH_2-H > C_6H_5-H > C_2H_5-H$$

We do not ordinarily think of hydrocarbons as acids, but a hydrocarbon can donate a proton to a suitably strong base. The RNa compounds fill the latter requirement, being far stronger bases than conventional bases (such as sodium hydroxide).

The order of acidities quoted in the preceding paragraph arises from several causes. Toluene ($C_6H_5CH_3$) is most acidic, because its resulting anion is stabilized by resonance:

This is analogous to the stabilization of the corresponding carbonium ion, discussed in Chap. 6. The additional benzene rings in $(C_6H_5)_2CH_2$ and $(C_6H_5)_3CH$ make them still more acidic than toluene. Benzene is more acidic than ethane because its carbon-hydrogen bonds are formed from sp^2, as opposed to sp^3, orbitals of carbon. The greater s character of the orbital means that the electrons are held closer to carbon, and the bond to hydrogen is weakened. A more striking example is found in the acetylenes (sp hybridization), which are sufficiently acidic to react with sodium directly:

$$2RC{\equiv}CH + 2Na \longrightarrow 2RC{\equiv}CNa + H_2$$

7.4 STRUCTURE OF THE GRIGNARD REAGENT

So far we have written the formula of the Grignard reagent as RMgX. It does behave in its chemical reactions as if it had this formula, but the actual species present in a solution of a Grignard reagent are still subject to dispute. In the following paragraphs we will summarize the evidence concerning the structures of Grignard reagents.

Solvation of the Grignard reagent is very important. The firmness with which the solvent is bound to the reagent is strikingly illustrated by the difficulty one finds in removing the last traces of solvent. A solution of a Grignard reagent in diethyl ether ($C_2H_5OC_2H_5$) still retains nearly one mole of ether per mole of reagent after drying for several hours at 150°, though the normal boiling point of ether is 35°! Diethyl ether is by far the most common solvent for Grignard reagents. In some cases, where higher temperatures or different solvent properties are desired, either of two cyclic ethers, tetrahydrofuran and dioxane, may be used. These have the structures:

tetrahydrofuran   dioxane

Returning to the structure of the Grignard reagent itself: It is possible to prepare a dialkylmagnesium by the indirect procedure:

$$(C_2H_5)_2Hg + Mg \longrightarrow (C_2H_5)_2Mg + Hg$$

If this diethylmagnesium is dissolved in ether containing an equimolar amount of magnesium bromide, the resulting solution behaves exactly like that obtained directly in the reaction:

$$C_2H_5Br + Mg \longrightarrow C_2H_5MgBr$$

This evidence led to the suggestion that the Grignard reagent was not a single substance, but an equilibrium mixture of several different species. The two most reasonable possibilities for the equilibrium are

$$2RMgX \rightleftharpoons R_2Mg + MgX_2$$

or

$$R_2Mg \cdot MgX_2 \rightleftharpoons R_2Mg + MgX_2$$

In the second equation, the dot signifies some sort of association of the R_2Mg and the MgX_2 molecules. It does not imply a direct bond between two magnesium atoms, for the association would be much more likely to involve Mg—X—Mg linkages.

For a long time, no distinction between these possibilities could be made. Recent evidence has at last begun to clarify the picture, though it is still far from complete. One very interesting study used radioactive magnesium as a tracer: If magnesium bromide containing radioactive magnesium is mixed with inactive diethylmagnesium, the first equation predicts

$$(C_2H_5)_2Mg + \overset{*}{M}gBr_2 \rightleftharpoons C_2H_5MgBr + C_2H_5\overset{*}{M}gBr$$

In this equation the reverse reaction is shown as giving the same species as those which were put in. The two molecules of C_2H_5MgBr are in fact identical except for the isotopic label, and could with equal probability react as follows:

$$C_2H_5MgBr + C_2H_5\overset{*}{M}gBr \rightleftharpoons (C_2H_5)_2\overset{*}{M}g + MgBr_2$$

We thus predict that the radioactivity should become evenly distributed between the magnesium bromide and the diethylmagnesium. In the second possible equilibrium the two magnesium atoms remain distinct from each other, and no "shuffling" is expected:

$$(C_2H_5)_2Mg \cdot \overset{*}{M}gBr \rightleftharpoons (C_2H_5)_2Mg + \overset{*}{M}gBr_2$$

In most cases the radioactivity is equilibrated between the magnesium bromide and the dialkylmagnesium, though equilibration did seem slow in experiments where an impure grade of magnesium was used. These facts favor the first equilibrium.

Another recent piece of evidence was based on an indirect method of measuring the vapor pressure of solutions of Grignard reagents. You will remember that the vapor pressure is a colligative property of a solution; i.e., it depends on the number of particles in the solution. If R_2Mg and MgX_2 associate to $R_2Mg \cdot MgX_2$, the number of particles will be decreased. The other possible equilibrium,

$$R_2Mg + MgX_2 \rightleftharpoons 2RMgX$$

produces no change in the number of particles.

Mixing solutions of diethyl magnesium and magnesium bromide in fact led to no apparent changes in the number of particles. Experiments were carried out in both ether and tetrahydrofuran solutions, and their results suggest that there is no appreciable association of diethylmagnesium and magnesium bromide. One reservation is necessary, however: the solutions were rather dilute, so that association may still occur in the more concentrated solutions normally used in synthetic work.

Even with all the evidence obtainable by modern experimental techniques (including that outlined above), we can say very little that is certain about the structures of Grignard reagents. Solutions of the reagents apparently consist mainly of dialkylmagnesium and magnesium halide in equilibrium with alkylmagnesium halide. The position of the equilibrium can only be estimated, and seems to depend on the solvent and on the nature of the Grignard reagent. Even if reliable values for the equilibrium constants were known, the species responsible for the reactions of Grignard reagents would not necessarily be obvious. For example, even if $RMgX$ were present in much lower concentration than R_2Mg, it could still be the only species undergoing reaction if it were much more reactive than R_2Mg.

The synthetic implication of all these studies, then, is that either $RMgX$ or R_2Mg (or both) may be the reactant under any given set of circumstances. In support of R_2Mg in at least some cases is the fact that certain reactions of Grignard reagents give better yields when *two* moles of reagent are used for each mole of the other reactant. This is just what would be expected if the reagent reacted as R_2Mg (*one* mole from *two* moles of RX) rather than RMgX (*one* mole from *one* mole of RX). It is always permissible for the sake of simplicity to write the Grignard reagent as RMgX in chemical equations, but there are obvious synthetic advantages in remembering that it sometimes behaves more like $R_2Mg + MgX_2$.

7.5 REACTIONS OF GRIGNARD REAGENTS

As mentioned before, Grignard reagents have very many uses in organic synthesis. We will not attempt to cover exhaustively the reactions of Grignard reagents. Entire books have been written on the subject whereas we have only a few pages to devote to it.

At the basis of any discussion of the reactions of Grignard reagents is the fact that they react as if their structure were

$$R^-MgX^+$$

This does not mean that there really are free carbanions in solutions of Grignard reagents. On the contrary, the alkyl group may always be held by partially covalent bonds to magnesium. The details of the mechanisms of Grignard reactions are probably quite complex. Nonetheless, the majority of Grignard reactions can be rationalized or even predicted on the assumption that the reagent acts as a carbanion donor.

One of the simplest reactions is that with so-called "active hydrogen" compounds. This term refers to almost any substance more able to donate a proton than the hydrocarbon RH corresponding to the Grignard RMgX. Some examples are

$$RMgX + HOH \longrightarrow RH + Mg(OH)X$$

$$RMgX + R'OH \longrightarrow RH + Mg(OR')X$$

$$RMg + NH_3 \longrightarrow RH + Mg(NH_2)X$$

$$RMgX + HX \longrightarrow RH + MgX_2$$

The reaction which occurs with water is the reason why moisture must be carefully excluded during the formation and reactions of Grignard reagents. The Zerevitinov determination of active hydrogen in organic compounds is based on reactions of this type. The procedure measures the volume of methane produced by reaction of the organic compound with a methyl Grignard reagent.

Most of these reactions with active hydrogen compounds are of little or no use synthetically. Among the exceptions is the reaction with acetylenes:

$$RMgX + R'C{\equiv}CH \longrightarrow R'C{\equiv}CMgX + RH$$

The resulting organometallic compound behaves as a Grignard reagent itself. This reaction constitutes another demonstration of the enhanced acidity of the sp carbon-hydrogen bonds of acetylene. Grignard reagents, incidentally, do not usually react with the sp^2 carbon-hydrogen bonds of benzene or alkenes, even though this is theoretically possible for an aliphatic Grignard reagent.

Grignard reagents can function as nucleophiles in displacements at carbon. We have already seen one example in Chap. 3: that is, the reaction with epoxides:

$$RMgX + CH_2\!\!-\!\!CH_2 \longrightarrow RCH_2CH_2OMgX$$
$$\underset{O}{\diagdown\diagup}$$

Analogous displacements can occur with sufficiently reactive alkyl halides, and some of these are of synthetic value:

$$C_6H_5MgBr + CH_2\!\!=\!\!CHCH_2Br \longrightarrow CH_2\!\!=\!\!CHCH_2C_6H_5$$

A bothersome side reaction in the preparation of certain Grignard reagents, especially those from benzyl and allyl halides, is coupling to produce a hydrocarbon. This reaction is probably a displacement by Grignard reagent on unreacted allyl halide:

$$C_6H_5CH_2MgCl + C_6H_5CH_2Cl \longrightarrow C_6H_5CH_2CH_2C_6H_5$$

Since halogens are electrophilic, we would expect them to react with the nucleophilic Grignard reagent:

$$RMgX + X_2 \longrightarrow RX + MgX_2$$

This reaction is sometimes used to convert one alkyl halide into another:

$$(CH_3)_2CHBr + Mg \longrightarrow (CH_3)_2CHMgBr$$
$$(CH_3)_2CHMgBr + I_2 \longrightarrow (CH_3)_2CHI$$

Another use is in analysis of a solution of a Grignard reagent. It is allowed to react with iodine, and the excess iodine titrated with thiosulfate.

Grignard reagents react readily with carbon dioxide to give salts of organic acids:

$$RMgX + CO_2 \longrightarrow RCOOMgX$$
$$\overset{\overset{\displaystyle O}{\|}}{RCOOMgX + HX \longrightarrow RCOH + MgX_2}$$

In fact, very many compounds containing carbon-oxygen or carbon-nitrogen double bonds will add Grignard reagents. An example is

$$R'MgX + R\!\!-\!\!\overset{\overset{\displaystyle O}{\|}}{C}\!\!-\!\!R \longrightarrow R\!\!-\!\!\overset{\overset{\displaystyle OMgX}{|}}{\underset{\underset{\displaystyle R'}{|}}{C}}\!\!-\!\!R \xrightarrow{H_2O} R\!\!-\!\!\overset{\overset{\displaystyle OH}{|}}{\underset{\underset{\displaystyle R'}{|}}{C}}\!\!-\!\!R$$

The alkyl group of the Grignard reagent always goes to the carbon end of the double bond. Such reactions are extremely useful in organic synthesis. We will not discuss them further here, as they belong more logically in another book of this series.†

An important group of reactions of Grignard reagents was described in Sec. 7.3: these are the reactions with halides of metals lower than magnesium in the electromotive series to give organometallic compounds of their metals. Analogous reactions occur with halides of certain non-metals; two examples are:

$$3RMgCl + PCl_3 \longrightarrow PR_3 + 3MgCl$$

$$4RMgCl + SiCl_4 \longrightarrow SiR_4 + 4MgCl$$

The product of the first reaction is called a *phosphine,* and of the second, a *silane.* The reactions can be stopped when only part of the halogen has been replaced, if less Grignard reagent is used:

$$2RMgCl + SiCl_4 \longrightarrow R_2SiCl_2 + 2MgCl_2$$

"Silicone" plastics result from reaction of these partially alkylated silicon halides with water:

$$R_2SiCl_2 + H_2O \longrightarrow \overset{\displaystyle R}{\underset{\displaystyle R}{-Si-}}O-\overset{\displaystyle R}{\underset{\displaystyle R}{Si-}}O-\overset{\displaystyle R}{\underset{\displaystyle R}{Si-}}O- + HCl$$

Other organometallic compounds will be treated much more briefly than the Grignard reagent. Organometallics of metals near magnesium in the periodic chart are fundamentally similar to Grignard reagents in their chemical properties. Organolithium compounds are somewhat more reactive than Grignard reagents, and are used successfully in certain reactions where the Grignard reagent gives poor yields or fails (notably, in additions to sterically-hindered carbonyl compounds). Organosodium and organopotassium compounds are little used. Organocadmium compounds are less reactive than Grignard reagents, and are used when one wants to avoid additions to carbon-oxygen double bonds:

$$(CH_3)_2Cd + 2R\overset{\displaystyle O}{\overset{\|}{C}}Cl \longrightarrow 2R\overset{\displaystyle O}{\overset{\|}{C}}CH_3 + CdCl_2$$

Organometallic compounds of the less reactive metals are of very little synthetic interest. We will give as examples a few reactions of organomercury compounds; these reactions have been of recent interest in studies of stereochemistry and mechanisms of electrophilic substitution. Two types

† C. D. Gutsche, *op. cit*

of organomercury compounds are known ($RHgX$ and R_2Hg); these can be made to equilibrate under appropriate conditions:

$$2RHgX \rightleftharpoons R_2Hg + HgX_2$$

The reaction can be forced to the right by removal of HgX_2 by reduction, or to the left by adding an excess of HgX_2. Note that these two reactions can be regarded as electrophilic attacks by the mercury atoms on the alkyl groups. Two other important electrophilic substitution reactions of organomercury compounds are:

$$RHgX + X_2 \longrightarrow RX + HgX_2$$

and

$$RHgR + HX \longrightarrow RH + RHgX$$

When the two R groups of $RHgR$ are not the same, two sets of products can result. These unsymmetrical compounds ($RHgR'$) have been used in studying the relative ease of cleavage of various alkyl-mercury bonds.

7.6 STEREOCHEMISTRY OF ELECTROPHILIC SUBSTITUTION

We noted in Chap. 3 that stereochemistry is a useful tool in studying the mechanisms of nucleophilic substitution reactions. For a long time there was very little systematic study of the stereochemistry of electrophilic substitution. Recent work has improved this situation to a great extent. Before taking up the evidence, we will discuss the theoretical possibilities.

A completely free alkyl carbanion would be expected to give racemic product. Unlike the planar, symmetrical carbonium ions, carbanions are pyramidal and therefore capable of asymmetry. The two enantiomers of an asymmetric carbanion are very rapidly interconverted, however, by a vibrational motion like that of an umbrella turning inside out:

This rapid inversion around an atom having an unshared pair of electrons was first noted with ammonia and the amines. An amine molecule is, of course, free of covalent bonding to other amine molecules or to solvent, and is a good model for a completely free carbanion. No optically-active amine (that is, with activity due to asymmetry at the *nitrogen* atom) has ever been isolated; this demonstrates that the inversion is very rapid.

A carbanion cannot be free in the same sense as an amine molecule, for the carbanion must always be associated with some positive ion. The question with an organometallic compound, then, is whether the carbon-metal bond has enough covalent character to prevent the inversion. The answer to this question depends on the nature of the metal.

Attempts to prepare Grignard reagents from optically-active alkyl halides have always led to racemic final products. Whether this racemization occurred during or after the formation of the Grignard reagent could not be absolutely decided from the evidence obtained. The data on organolithium compounds, which we will consider next, suggest that any optical activity present in a Grignard reagent at the time of its formation would rapidly disappear under the conditions normally used for its preparation.

Optically-active 2-octyllithium retains some of its activity when prepared at $-70°$ in a hydrocarbon solvent containing a little ether. At $0°C$, complete racemization results. Optical rotation was not measured on the 2-octyllithium itself, but on its carbonation product:

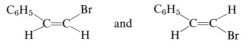

A more extensive investigation of optically-active 2-butyllithium revealed these facts: In a pure hydrocarbon solvent, at least some optical activity is retained for as long as an hour. At $-40°$, over 80% of the optical activity remains after four hours. Addition of some ether to the hydrocarbon solvent makes the racemization take place much faster.

There is evidently a great deal of ionic character to the carbon-lithium bond, and only low temperatures or non-polar solvents can keep it from dissociating sufficiently to permit racemization. Any alkyl-metal compounds derived from alkali or alkaline-earth metals can probably be expected to racemize rather easily.

If the metal is attached to an unsaturated atom, configuration does not seem to be lost quite so readily. The Grignard reagents from *cis*- and *trans*-2-bromostyrene,

give different mixtures of the corresponding acids on carbonation. The *cis*-bromide gives about 70% *cis*-acid, while the *trans*-bromide gives about 60% *trans*-acid. Though extensive interconversion occurs, there is some retention of configuration. The lithium compounds,

are only slowly interconverted in benzene-pentane mixtures around $0°$. Higher temperatures, or large proportions of ether, promote interconversion, but the configuration is clearly much more stable than it is at a saturated carbon atom. There does not seem to be any simple explanation for this phenomenon, though it is also found in nitrogen compounds. Oximes, for example, have quite stable isomers analogous to the *cis* and *trans* isomers of olefins:

A carbanion may also be generated by removing a proton from an organic compound. Saturated hydrocarbons are normally very poor proton donors, so proton loss is usually facilitated by using compounds that can give resonance-stabilized carbanions. Also, recapture of a proton by the carbanion simply regenerates starting material. In order to follow the extent of reaction, a reactant containing deuterium is placed in a solvent containing hydrogen. Since the solvent is in large excess, reaction of the carbanion with solvent places hydrogen where deuterium originally was. Such an experiment is outlined below:

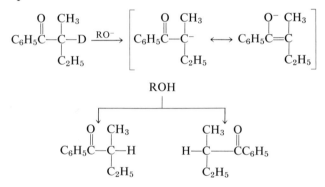

The intermediate carbanion in this case is planar, for the negatively charged carbon atom must be sp^2 hybridized so that the unshared electron pair will occupy a p orbital that can overlap effectively the π orbital of the carbon-oxygen double bond. This planar configuration means equal probability of protonation on either side of the plane, and hence a racemic product. The observed rates of deuterium loss and racemization are in fact the same.

Numerous experiments of this type led to the belief that resonance-stabilized carbanions would give racemic products under all conditions. More recent work has shown that this is not true. Cram† and his co-workers have examined the stereochemistry of many carbanion reactions, and have found cases ranging from predominant retention to predominant

---

† D. J. Cram. Born 1919. American. Professor of Chemistry at University of California at Los Angeles. Stereochemistry of carbonium-ion reactions (see Sec. 6.4 for a summary of his work on 3-phenyl-2-butyl derivatives) and of electrophilic aliphatic substitution.

inversion of configuration. A simple example is deuterium exchange by 2-phenylbutane:

$$C_6H_5{-}\underset{\underset{C_2H_5}{|}}{\overset{\overset{CH_3}{|}}{C}}{-}D + ROH \xrightarrow{RO^-} C_6H_5{-}\underset{\underset{C_2H_5}{|}}{\overset{\overset{CH_3}{|}}{C}}{-}H + ROD$$

The intermediate carbanion is resonance-stabilized because the negative charge can be distributed into the benzene ring:

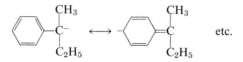 etc.

The stereochemistry of the exchange depends strongly on the solvent. Potassium *t*-butoxide in *t*-butyl alcohol gives mainly *retention*. Apparently the carbanion picks up a proton from the *front* side very rapidly after the deuterium atom is removed. The proton donor is probably a *t*-butyl alcohol molecule involved in the solvation of the potassium ion.

In dimethyl sulfoxide [$(CH_3)_2SO$] containing potassium *t*-butoxide and a little *t*-butyl alcohol, *racemization* results. The much lower concentration of the proton donor enables the carbanion to last long enough to become symmetrically solvated. The situation is very similar to that discussed in Chap. 3 for the S_N1 reaction.

Finally, diethylene glycol ($HOCH_2CH_2OCH_2CH_2OH$) plus its potassium salt as base gives mainly *inversion*. In this more strongly ionizing solvent, the free anion of the base removes the deuteron. At the same time, the high "concentration" of hydroxyl groups in the diethylene glycol solvent means that one will almost always be close to the back of the carbon. Thus, a proton can be donated to the back of the carbon atom at the same time that the deuteron is removed (or very shortly thereafter).

The deuterium-exchange reactions just described all presumably involve carbanions, though in some cases very short-lived ones. Thus, they are S_E1 reactions. The stereochemistry of the S_E2 reaction appears to be simpler: for example, treatment of 2-butylmercuric bromide results in uptake of radioactivity by the organomercury compound with *retention* of optical activity:

$$H{-}\underset{\underset{C_2H_5}{|}}{\overset{\overset{CH_3}{|}}{C}}{-}HgBr + \overset{*}{H}gBr_2 \longrightarrow H{-}\underset{\underset{C_2H_5}{|}}{\overset{\overset{CH_3}{|}}{C}}{-}\overset{*}{H}gBr + HgBr_2$$

Several similar reactions also proceed with retention; this will probably be the general rule for S_E2 reactions. We would expect the electrophilic reagent to prefer attack at a point of high electron density. Since the electrons are obviously concentrated in the bond to the leaving group, front-side attack should be preferred.

In this final chapter, we have discussed a field that is less thoroughly explored than most of those covered in previous chapters. Much of the information given is the result of very recent research; some aspects of the field that may appear to have been slighted are simply too tentative as yet for a simple summary. Relative reactivities in S_E2 reactions, for example, are not very regular, and the contributions of electronic and steric factors to this situation are unknown. Textbooks, including this one, tend to concentrate on the settled and well-understood areas of a subject. A reminder that much is still unsettled and poorly understood may balance the impressions given in the preceding text and leave the reader with a picture that is closer to reality.

CHAPTER 7 REVIEW QUESTIONS

1. Describe the S_E1 and S_E2 mechanisms, and compare them in as many ways as you can with the S_N1 and S_N2 mechanisms.

2. Rank in order of acidity: toluene, ethylbenzene, isopropylbenzene, t-butylbenzene, diphenylmethane and triphenylmethane. Give reasons for the order you give.

3. Outline the existing evidence on the structure of the Grignard reagent.

4. What conditions would you choose to obtain the highest optical activity possible in the product of carbonation of 2-butyllithium? Explain the reasons for your choice.

5. Why does optically-active phenyl 2-butyl ketone racemize when treated with base in a hydroxylic solvent?

6. Given any organic compounds of three carbon atoms or less, and any inorganic reagents, devise practical laboratory syntheses for the following:

(a) $(CH_3)_2CHCH_2CH_2OH$

(b) $(CH_3)_2CHCH_2OH$

(c) $CH_3COCH_2CH_2CH_3$

(d) $HC\equiv C-\underset{\underset{\displaystyle }{|}}{\overset{\overset{\displaystyle OH}{|}}{C}}(CH_3)_2$

Suggested Further Readings

Many treatments of reaction mechanisms on a more advanced level are available. Most of these cover organic reactions in general, but contain chapters on the particular reaction types we have discussed. Books organized in terms of reaction types and oriented toward synthetic applications are few, but one good one is listed below. Most of the treatments of mechanisms presuppose some knowledge of physical chemistry. This should not be an insurmountable obstacle to understanding, however, since little knowledge of the more abstruse or mathematical side of physical chemistry is required.

Hine, Jack, *Physical Organic Chemistry* (2nd ed.). New York: McGraw-Hill Book Co., Holt, Reinhart and Winston, Inc., 1962. An excellent, well-balanced general text on mechanisms.

Gould, E. S., *Mechanism and Structure in Organic Chemistry*. New York: 1959. A somewhat more qualitative and less rigorous coverage of the same ground as Hine.

Ingold, C. K., *Structure and Mechanism in Organic Chemistry*. Ithaca, New York: Cornell University Press, 1953. A real classic, describing the research and the ideas of an outstanding scholar. Not easy reading for a beginner, but well worth the effort.

Fuson, R. C., *Reactions of Organic Compounds*. New York: John Wiley and Sons, Inc., 1962. A more detailed treatment of synthetic methods than is given in elementary textbooks.

Bunton, C. A., *Nucleophilic Substitution at a Saturated Carbon Atom*. New York: Elsevier Publishing Company, 1963. A detailed treatment of mechanism. Part of a series edited by E. D. Hughes: *Reaction Mechanisms in Organic Chemistry*.

Banthorpe, D. V., *Elimination Reactions*. New York: Elsevier Publishing Company, 1963. A third volume in the series mentioned above.

Index